D0427055

MEDIA CENTER
PHILLIPS JR. HIGH SCHOOL
3825 GENERAL AVENUE
BILLINGS, MT. 59102

PLUMBERS AND PIPE FITTERS LIBRARY
Volume III

Water Supply
Drainage • Calculations

by Charles McConnell
revised by Tom Philbin

MEDIA CENTER
BILLINGS VO-TECH CENTER
3803 CENTRAL AVENUE
BILLINGS, MT 59102

WITHDRAWN

THEODORE AUDEL & CO.
a division of
G. K. Hall & Co.
Boston, Massachusetts

THIRD EDITION
SECOND PRINTING

Copyright © 1967 and 1977 by
Howard W. Sams & Co., Inc.
Copyright © 1983 by The Bobbs-Merrill Co., Inc.

All rights reserved.
No part of this publication may be reproduced, stored in a retrieval system or
transmitted in any form or by any means, mechanical, electronic, photocopying,
recording or otherwise without the prior written permission of the publisher.

For information, address G. K. Hall & Co., 70 Lincoln Street,
Boston, MA 02111

Published by G. K. Hall & Co.
A publishing subsidiary of ITT

Manufactured in the United States of America

Library of Congress Cataloging in Publication Data

McConnell, Charles.
  Plumbers and pipe fitters library.

  Includes indexes.
    1. Plumbing—Handbooks, manuals, etc. 2. Pipefitting—Handbooks,
manuals, etc. I. Philbin, Tom, 1934-   II. Title.
  TH6125.M4   1984   696'.1   83-6384
  ISBN 0-672-23385-1 (v. 1)
  ISBN 0-672-23386-X (v.2)
  ISBN 0-672-23387-8 (v.3)
  ISBN 0-672-23384-3 (set)

Foreword

Plumbing and pipe fitting play a major role in the construction of every residential, commercial, and industrial building. Of all the building trades, none is as essential to the health and well-being of the community in general, and the building occupants in particular, as the plumbing trade. It is the responsibility of anyone involved in the installation of the plumbing materials and equipment to uphold this trust.

Every plumbing installation is governed by certain rules and regulations set forth in local plumbing codes that have been adopted from standards established at a local, state, or federal level. In addition, each installation is subject to inspection by a licensed inspector to ensure that all rules and regulations have been complied with. All this, coupled with the practice of requiring those persons engaged in plumbing installation to pass an examination for a license, shows the great importance placed on the trades.

This series of books has been written to aid persons who wish to become plumbers, as well as those who are already doing the job, plus the do-it-yourselfer. This, the third of three volumes, deals with water-supply systems and with drainage and sewage-disposal systems. The simple mathematics and physics necessary for a complete understanding of the material in the rest of the library are included. This final volume also contains chapters of general plumbing information and questions and answers containing the solutions to many common plumbing problems.

Contents

CHAPTER 5

CHAPTER 6

CHAPTER 7

CHAPTER 8

CHAPTER 9

CHAPTER 1

Water Supply

City water systems obtain their water from several sources—lakes, wells, and reservoirs fed by rivers and creeks. Except in relatively small communities, wells are an uncertain main source of supply. In larger cities, well water is primarily used to assist in meeting peak demand periods and to temper the supply from lakes or reservoirs. For example, the addition of well water at an average temperature of 55° to water from a lake or reservoir that may be 35° or colder warms the colder water and helps eliminate water-main breakages. A typical well and pump used for these purposes is shown in Fig. 1-1.

Cities that depend upon water from creeks or rivers may find that the supply is ample in the spring of the year, due to melting snow and spring rains, but not during summer and fall. Water from these sources must be conserved and stored for future use. Reservoirs are built for this, and a dam is built at the lower end of the reservoir to impound the water. Reservoirs are designed to main-

Courtesy Indianapolis Water Co.

Fig. 1-1. A well and pump for a city water system.

tain a certain maximum level; flood gates are built into the dam to permit the release of excess water if the level becomes too high. Reservoirs also assist in flood control by storing water that would otherwise cause flooding for slow release later. Besides storing water for future use, they may also serve as recreational spots. A typical reservoir of this type is shown in Fig. 1-2.

Water stored in the reservoirs is "raw" water, unfit in almost all

Courtesy Indianapolis Water Co.

Fig. 1-2. Aerial view of Morse Reservoir, one of several reservoirs serving the Indianapolis area.

cases for human consumption. The water utility, starting with the raw water, filters and chemically treats the water to make it potable. Fig. 1-3 shows the various stages of treatment and testing as raw water from a reservoir is processed and delivered to its consumers.

Raw water entering a treatment plant usually contains minerals, silt, sand, and other biologic organisms. In normal processing, little is done to remove the dissolved salts such as limestone; the emphasis is on removing the suspended matter. As the water enters the plant a coagulant, aluminum sulphate (alum), is added; this chemical combines with water to form aluminum hydroxide, a visible-sized gelatinous mass called "floc." Immediately after the alum is added to the incoming water, the mixture enters a large mixing basin. Large paddles rotate slowly in the water to thoroughly mix the chemical with the water. After mixing, the water moves into the settling portion of the basin. There is no agitation in this portion of the basin; the water is moving very slowly, and the

9

floc particles, with the added weight of the suspended material in the water, settle to the bottom. This process removes 95 percent of the foreign particulate matter. At the end of the basin weirs, (dams) at the water's surface allow the upper-level, higher-quality water to pass on to the next stage of treatment, the filtering basin.

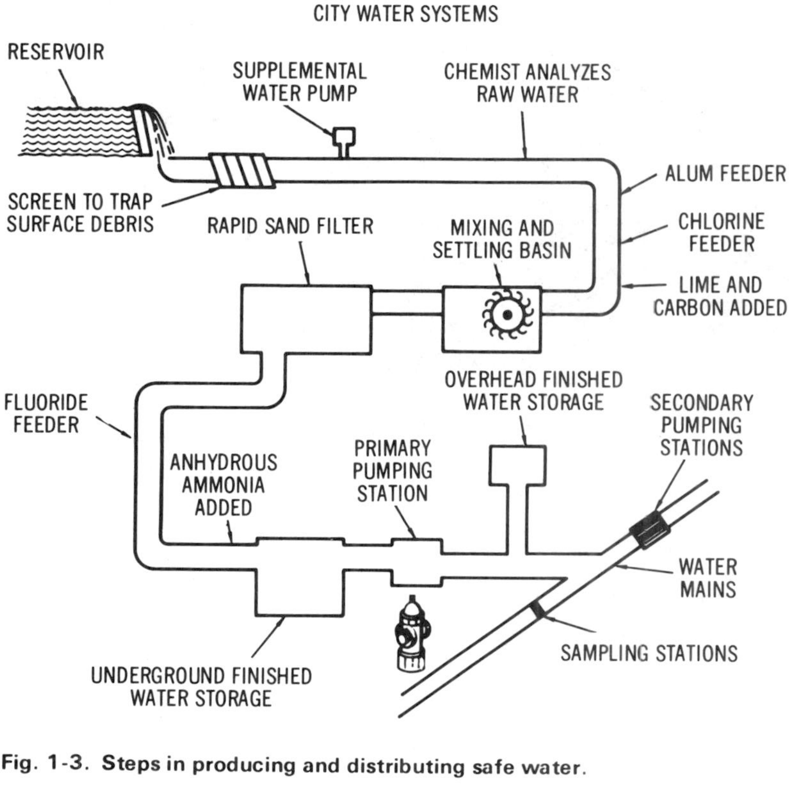

CITY WATER SYSTEMS

Fig. 1-3. Steps in producing and distributing safe water.

A filter is another concrete box with a series of pipes that brings the settled water to the filter. Within the filter lies an underdrain collection system for the filtered water. Above the collection system lies 24 to 30 inches of fine sand and anthracite (fine coal) supported by five layers of graded gravel. Water from the settling basin passes down through the filter sand and gravel. Here all but the finest colloidal particles are removed, and clear water leaves the filter bed. A certain percentage of harmful bacteria is also removed in the filtering bed. A typical filter bed is shown in Fig. 1-4.

After filtration and clarification, the raw water enters the chemical treatment tank for sterilization with chlorine. Chlorine is added to the raw water before it enters the mixing basin. The chlorine is thoroughly dispersed through the raw water in the mixing basin, and sufficient contact time is provided in the mixing and settling basins and filters to ensure an effective bacteriological kill. The chlorine oxidizes certain inorganic and organic matter; it also acts as a decolorizer and removes some of the objectionable tastes and odors. The amount of chlorine used is in direct relation to the pollution level of the raw water. The maximum residual level of chlorine in the potable water leaving the plant is 1 part per million. Anhydrous ammonia is another chemical regularly used in water treatment. It is added as the water leaves the sand filter, and it combines with the chlorine to reduce taste and odor problems.

In some water systems another chemical, fluoride, at a level of 1 part per million is added to reduce the incidence of tooth decay in children. A fluoride feeder is shown in Fig. 1-5. The water that entered the plant as raw water has now been screened, filtered, and chemically treated to render it safe for human consumption.

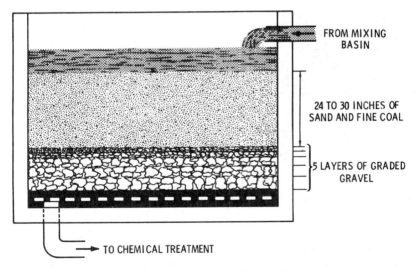

FROM MIXING BASIN

24 TO 30 INCHES OF SAND AND FINE COAL

5 LAYERS OF GRADED GRAVEL

TO CHEMICAL TREATMENT

Fig. 1-4. Details of construction of a sand filter bed.

11

Fig. 1-5. A chemical feeder controls the addition of fluoride to water.

WATER STORAGE

Water that has been purified must be stored for use during periods of peak demand. Large underground finished water reservoirs similar to the one shown in Fig. 1-6 are often used for this purpose. In addition, water towers similar to the one shown in Fig. 1-7 are used, not only to maintain a reserve supply for use during peak demand periods but also to maintain pressure in the distribution mains. Water from the distribution mains can be

Courtesy Indianapolis Water Co.

Fig. 1-6. An underground finished water storage reservoir.

pumped into the tower at night, during periods of low demand, for use during the day at peak demand. The stored water helps maintain a constant even pressure. A column of water one foot high exerts a pressure of .433 lbs. per sq. in. at its base. Therefore, the water in a tower 100 ft. high will exert 43.3 lbs. of pressure through the vertical riser to a point at ground level. If the distribution main is 5 ft. below ground level, the tower water will exert 45.465 lbs. of pressure on the main. Water towers in larger cities are usually placed at strategic points to ensure a plentiful supply during periods of peak demand.

13

Courtesy Indianapolis Water Co.

Fig. 1-7. An overhead water storage tank.

DISTRIBUTION MAINS

When the raw water has been "finished," or purified, it must be sent to the users through underground distribution mains. Over a period of years, various materials have been used in the manufacturing of underground water mains; cast iron has proven to be the most durable. Cast iron rusts on the surface but protects itself against the continued rusting that would, in time, destroy the metal. Indeed, when cast iron rusts on the surface, the granular rust coating adheres strongly to the metal and protects unrusted parts from further corrosive action. A type of cast iron called ductile iron is widely used for water mains; it has the advantage of being more flexible, less brittle, than ordinary cast-iron piping. Fig. 1-8 shows workmen installing cast-iron water mains.

Courtesy Suffolk County Water Authority

Fig. 1-8. Workmen installing main pipe.

In order to maintain a constant pressure on distribution mains throughout the area served by the water utility, primary pumping stations, similar to the one shown in Fig. 1-9, are used to start the water on its way through the mains. Secondary pumping stations are located at strategic points to boost the pressure when necessary to ensure a steady flow throughout the system. Fire hydrants are

15

placed at regular intervals on the distribution mains, making water under pressure readily available for use in emergencies.

Courtesy Indianapolis Water Co.

Fig. 1-9. A primary water pumping station.

WATER TESTING

A modern water utility makes many tests daily, both on raw and finished water. Finished water is tested at widely scattered points throughout the system to maintain the highest standards of purity. Fig. 1-10 shows a chemist examining a water sample.

Chemicals used regularly but not necessarily continuously in water treatment are:

Copper sulphate to control algae and other biologic organisms.
Lime to increase the alkalinity and pH° during periods of high stream flow.
Carbon for taste and odor control.
Sulphur dioxide as a dechlorinating agent.
°pH—a measure of the acidity or alkalinity of water.

16

Courtesy Indianapolis Water Co.

Fig. 1-10. A chemist tests water samples.

WELLS

The use of surface water, other than that collected on roofs or other controlled areas and stored in cisterns for rural domestic use,

17

presents many difficulties and should be avoided. Wells, of course, may be used. In terms of construction, they may be classified in the following groups:

1. Dug.
2. Bored.
3. Driven.
4. Drilled.

Dug Wells

A dug well is constructed by excavating a shaft, generally manually, and installing a casing where needed. Dug wells are used extensively for domestic water supplies. They are generally not very deep because they cannot readily be sunk far enough below the water table. Most are less than 50 feet deep. They generally yield only small supplies of water from water-bearing materials of rather low permeability near the top of the zone of saturation.

Dug wells are necessarily relatively large in cross-section, and they have correspondingly large storage capacity for each foot that they extend below the water table. Because of their shallow penetration into the zone of saturation, many dug wells fail in times of drought when the water table is reduced. A dug well is illustrated in Fig. 1-11.

Bored Wells

A bored well is constructed by boring a hole with a hand or power auger and installing tile or other casing. Bored wells range in diameter from only a few inches when hand-operated augers are used, to 4 feet or more when power augers are used. Like dug wells, bored ones do not extend into or through hard rock, and most of them are not sunk far into the zone of saturation. To a great extent bored wells resemble dug wells in that they generally have relatively small yield and are quite often affected by drought.

Driven Wells

A driven well is constructed by driving a pipe (usually equipped with a well point and screen) with a maul, drive donkey, or pile driver. Driven wells are confined to localities where water-

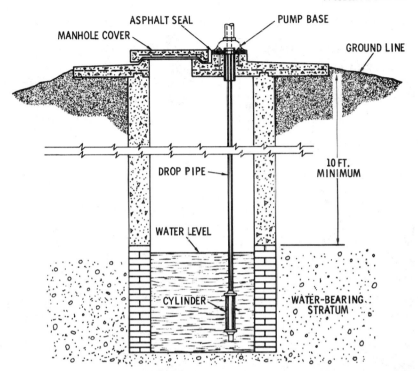

Fig. 1-11. Construction details of a dug well.

bearing sand or fine gravel lies at comparatively shallow depths, and where there are no intervening hard rocks or boulders that would prevent driving the pipe. Under these conditions, driven wells can be constructed rapidly and at small cost. The pipes used are normally 2 inches or less in diameter. These wells are usually pumped by suction from pumps located at the top of the pipe. Wells of this type are likely to be impractical if the sand or gravel has low permeability, but if the permeability is high, the well may be plentiful.

Drilled Wells

A drilled well is constructed by making a hole with a drilling machine and installing casing and a screen where needed. The excavating may be done by percussion or rotary tools or by jetting,

19

and the materials may be brought up by means of a boiler or hollow-drill tool or by a hydraulic process.

In the percussion well-drilling method, a heavy drill bit is suspended in a prepared hole in the ground by means of a wire rope attached at the upper end to the walking beam of a derrick. The bit is alternately lifted and dropped by the machinery, pounding the earth and rock into small fragments for subsequent removal from the hole.

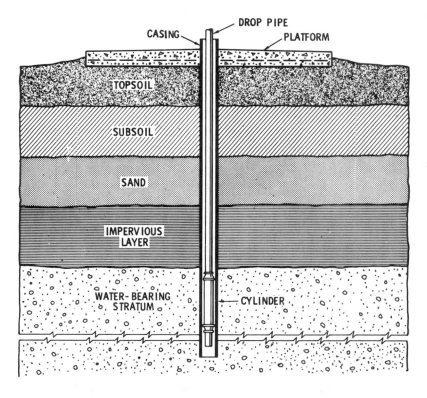

Fig. 1-12. Cross-sectional view of a drilled well, showing its path through several layers of soil.

Drilling methods have a great advantage over digging, boring, and driving methods because they are adapted for sinking the holes to water-bearing beds that may be far below the water table. Drilled wells are more apt to tap water supplies that might not be

20

recoverable with wells of other types, and as a rule they have larger yields and are less affected by drought. A drilled well is shown in Fig. 1-12.

CITY WATER SOURCES

The sources from which city water is obtained for domestic purposes are numerous, such as wells, springs, lakes, rivers, and rainfall. There are several methods of getting the water to the point of supply, such as:

1. Street pressure.
2. Pneumatic.
3. Electric.

Street Pressure System

The source of supply of the street pressure system is the street main into which water is furnished under pressure by the water company. A *service pipe* is run from the main to the dwelling and connects to the *supply pipe*, and from there suitable branches are run to the various fixtures, as shown in Fig. 1-13. Although this system is mechanically simple, it sometimes has disadvantages that depend on the pressure. Where the pressure is excessive, the piping and fixtures are subjected to needless pressure, causing excessive load on the valves and tending to increase leakage; if the pressure is too low or variable, the water may not flow to the outlets on the upper floors.

Sometimes, when the pressure is excessive, a reducing valve is placed on the supply pipe to protect the line and fittings from unnecessary pressure. It should be understood that, in any system, the installation must withstand not only the working pressure but also momentary shocks due to water hammer caused by the quick closing of faucets. The weight of the pipe used must be adequate for the working pressure. Because of the enormous strain possible from water hammer, and because of general deterioration from use, it is advisable to use pipe that when new, will have a pressure rating that is far in excess of working pressure.

21

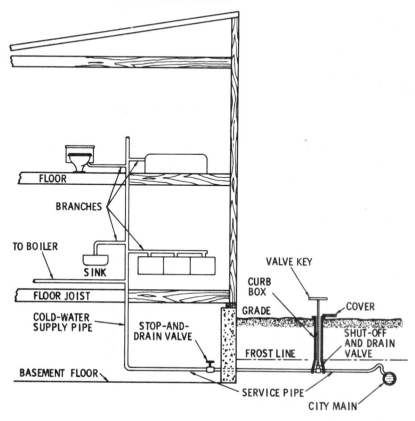

Fig. 1-13. A typical cold-water supply line.

Pneumatic System

The word *pneumatic* is defined as pertaining to devices that make use of compressed air. Accordingly, the pneumatic system of a water supply makes use of compressed air to elevate the water to the various outlets in a building. The apparatus required consists essentially of a closed cylindrical steel tank and a pump for raising the water from the source of supply and forcing it into the tank. When there is no water in the tank, it contains air at atmospheric pressure, or 14.7 lbs. per sq. in. In operation, the pumping of water into the bottom of the tank will compress the air after the opening into the tank has been closed. As the air is lighter than water, it is compressed into the space above the water. As the water level rises at each stroke of the pump, the air becomes compressed more and more in the top of the tank until it finally reaches the desired point of compression. The very strong pressure pushes the water out from the tank and through the pipes to any part of the house or grounds, where it is then ready to flow. Air is very elastic and acts much like a wound-up spring. Its force becomes less when the volume of water decreases and the air space expands. By increasing or decreasing the amount of air put into the tank, and also the pressure, pneumatic systems will meet the requirements of various locations requiring either a high or low pressure.

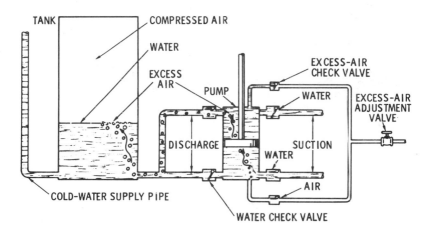

Fig. 1-14. A pneumatic water system.

There should be an air-charging device provided so that additional air is pumped into the tank at each stroke of the pump, if desired. This device usually consists of an air valve and a check valve attached to the cylinder head, as shown in Fig. 1-14. A small quantity of air is forced into the tank at each stroke of the pump to maintain the tank pressure. The amount of air pumped may be controlled by adjusting the air valve. Normally, and for ordinary elevations, little or no air is required.

POWER PUMPS

In selecting a water pump, consideration first must be given to its duty and to whether the pump possesses sufficient capacity to supply the home with the desired quantity up to the yield of the well. Pumps employed for water pumping may be classified with respect to their cycle of operation as:

1. Plunger or reciprocating.
2. Turbine.
3. Centrifugal.
4. Rotary.
5. Ejector.

They may also be divided into *shallow-* and *deep-well* pumps. Shallow-well pumps are sometimes referred to as *lift* or *suction* pumps. The plunger-type pump is occasionally termed a *positive-displacement* pump. The rotary pump is also a positive-displacement pump. Such pumps will continue to build up pressure as long as they continue to operate.

Centrifugal and ejector pumps develop pressure by centrifugal force and cease to build up pressure beyond a given limit. This limit depends on the design and speed. The pressure beyond which these pumps will not force water is termed the *shut-off* head. The discharge from centrifugal pumps can be regulated by means of a valve in the discharge pipe, but it should not be completely stopped in this manner.

Other mechanical means of lifting water are air-lift and air-displacement pumps, chain pumps, propeller and screw-type pumps, hydraulic rams, and siphon pumps. Air-lift and air-displacement pumps are usually not efficient and are therefore not often used. Chain pumps are not considered as sanitary as other force pumps and are also inefficient. The propeller or screw-type pumps are used for lower lifts and larger volume than are ordinarily required for domestic use. Hydraulic rams obtain their power from the water supply, and are wasteful, although completely automatic. The hydraulic ram is probably the most inefficient of the mechanical means mentioned above, if the quantity of water delivered is compared with the quantity of water required to supply it.

24

Turbine Pumps

The turbine pump is very simple in construction and consists essentially of one or more circular disks, as shown in Fig. 1-15. The outer edges of the disks are fitted with a series of equally spaced vanes or blades. The disks are firmly mounted on a drive shaft, while the assembly is surrounded by a close-fitting envelope or case. In operation, the disk rotates, with very little clearance, in a channel formed by the casing liners. Rotation of the disk forces the water to move with it, carrying the water from the inlet to the discharge line. Turbine pumps may be mounted with the shaft either vertically or horizontally.

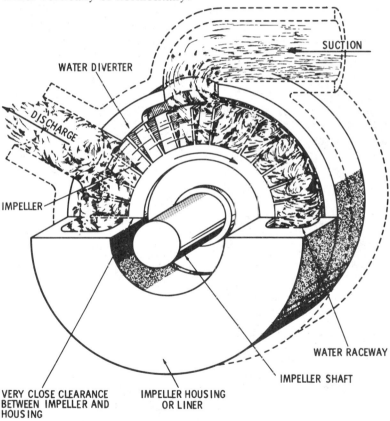

Fig. 1-15. The working principles of a turbine water pump.

The horizontal-type pump is often installed in shallow wells, but in deep wells the motor is mounted vertically and the shaft extends down below the water level. In some wells, one impeller may not develop sufficient pressure to deliver water to the surface of the well and against the pressure of the tank. In such cases, additional impellers are used in sufficient numbers to develop the desired pressure. Turbine units equipped with two impellers are termed *double-stage* turbine pumps, and if there are many impellers, they are called *multi-stage* turbine pumps.

Centrifugal Pumps

A centrifugal pump is different from a turbine pump. Instead of having the open blades mounted on the outside rim of a disk, in a centrifugal pump a number of vanes radiate from the hub, as in Fig. 1-16. The impeller operates in a close-fitted housing adapted to the particular form or forms of vanes used. The water enters the impeller from one or both sides at the hub, and is thrown out by centrifugal force. The casing has a volute (snail-like) passage extending around the impellers. This passage begins very small and increases in cross-sectional area to the discharge. Water moving out through the impeller creates a vacuum at the center.

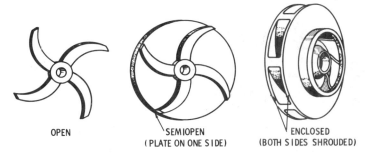

OPEN   SEMIOPEN
(PLATE ON ONE SIDE)   ENCLOSED
(BOTH SIDES SHROUDED)

Fig. 1-16. Various forms of vanes used in centrifugal pumps.

To use centrifugal force in a pump, there must be an impeller, a pump body, and a source of water. When the motor is turned on and the impeller starts to rotate at high speed, water is forced from the center of the impeller, out through the edge of the ports through an area known as the volute passages, and into the pump body. As this water is thrown out, atmospheric pressure on the surface of the well forces water up through the suction pipe into this area to relieve the partial vacuum.

Centrifugal pumps of the conventional type must be primed. They are not designed for high-suction lifts and are therefore usually set near the water's surface and operated with foot valves that keep water in the suction pipe. The pressure at the discharge end depends on the speed and diameter of the impeller.

The volume depends to a great extent on the width of the impeller and the size of the water passage. Centrifugal pumps are water-lubricated and are thus subject to excessive wear if the water carries abrasive material. If the water is free from such material, centrifugal pumps will last a long time. Centrifugal pumps, like rotary pumps, may be set with the shaft either horizontal or vertical. They also take their designations from the position of the shaft.

Rotary Pumps

The rotary pump is frequently called a *gear* pump because of its design, which is in the form of two gears. These gears mesh together inside the pump housing, as shown in Fig. 1-17. This type of pump is seldom used in domestic water-supply systems, but is used a great deal in pumping oil or other lubricating liquids that are free from abrasive materials. The liquid enters at the bottom

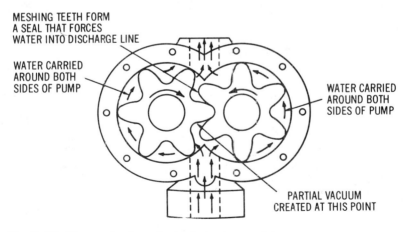

Fig. 1-17. The mechanism of a typical rotary pump.

27

(Fig 1-17), fills the space between the teeth, and is carried out around the top, where it is forced out when the teeth mesh with those of the opposite gear. The pump delivers a steady flow of liquid without pulsation, and since it is a positive-action type, it will operate against any pressure the equipment allows.

Ejector Pumps

The ejector, or jet, pump is relatively simple in construction and has a high capacity under low-pressure conditions. It is used in

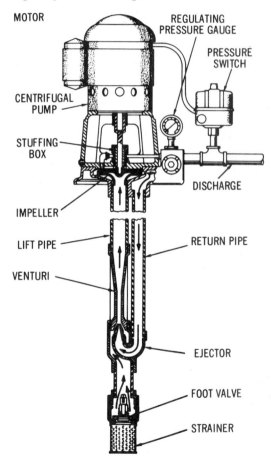

Fig. 1-18. The principle of operation of an ejector or jet-type pump.

both shallow and deep wells to the depth of 80 feet or more. The pumping mechanism usually consists of a vertical centrifugal or turbine pump, of the type previously discussed, operated in connection with a jet which is set up in the well.

The ejector pump is actually two pumps working together, one discharging into the other. This shown in Fig. 1-18. A cross-sectional view of the pump shows that, when properly primed and running, it delivers a given quantity of water to the surface by suction. At the discharge end, some water is forced into the pressure-tank line and some water returns to the jet, or ejector, nozzle.

Submersible Pumps

In a water system of this type, the entire pumping unit is submerged in the water in the well. This relatively new addition to the pump family is designed for deep-well installations and consists essentially of a pump and motor built together into a long slender unit. The motor is placed directly below the pumping unit, and a waterproof electric cable furnishes power to the motor.

It should be kept in mind that a submersible pump requires an ample supply of water and that the well must be free from sand in suspension. In common with other centrifugal pumping systems, a quantity of sand will quickly ruin both the pump and the motor. The submersible pump is somewhat more sensitive to sand and grit, mainly because of the great precision necessary in its construction.

CHAPTER 2

Drainage and Venting

The drainage and vent piping of a building is divided into several sections; building drain, soil and waste stacks, and vent stacks or vent piping.

The building drain is that part of the lowest piping of a drainage system which receives the discharge of soil, waste, or other drainage piping inside the building and conveys it outside the building to the building sewer. The exact distance that the building drain extends outside the building depends on the local code governing the installation; it may vary from two to ten feet. Most plumbing codes require a cleanout connection at or near the point where the building drain enters the building. Fig. 2-1 is a line drawing of the waste and vent piping in a home.

When a fixture drains into a pipe that also serves as a vent for another fixture, that vent is then termed a *wet* vent. Most codes permit wet venting under certain specified conditions.

Plumbing codes establish the maximum developed length of the fixture drain from the trap weir to the vent fitting. These codes

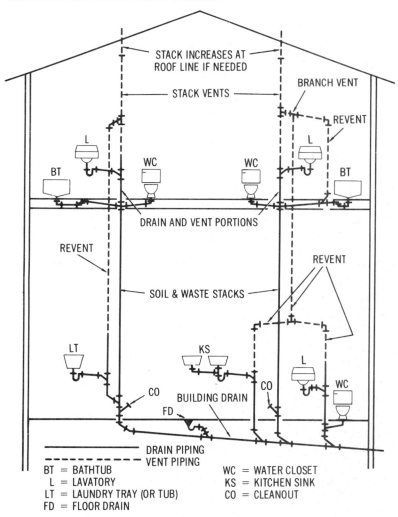

Fig. 2-1. Soil, waste, and vent piping in a home.

often vary slightly from one state or area to another. Fig. 2-1 shows the vent piping that would be required if the bathtub drain length exceeded the maximum distance permitted by a local code.

Proper venting prevents siphoning of traps by maintaining atmospheric pressure throughout the soil and waste piping and thus preventing the temporary formation of a vacuum in the drainage piping. Proper venting also allows any back pressure from the drainage system to be relieved through the vent piping and thus protects the trap seals.

Fig. 2-2A shows the drainage and vent piping for a battery of water closets. Each double wye has an individual vent connected

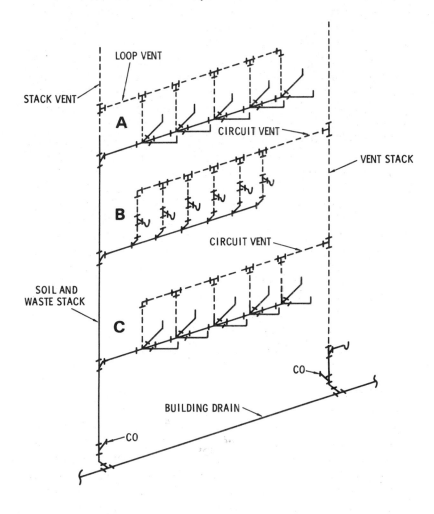

Fig. 2-2. The difference between loop and circuit vents.

to a *loop* vent. Fig. 2-2B shows the drainage and vent piping for a battery of lavatories. Each individual vent connects into a *circuit* vent. Fig. 2-2C shows a battery of water closets with each individual vent connected into a circuit vent. Note that Fig. 2-2B and Fig. 2-2C circuit vents connect into a *vent stack*. It is desirable to discharge the waste from a fixture such as a lavatory into the vent stack in order to wash the base of the stack.

Fig. 2-3 shows a garage-type floor drain. Greases, oils, and gasoline or other inflammable material float to the top where they can be skimmed off. This type of drain is designed to permit only water from near the bottom to enter the drainage piping.

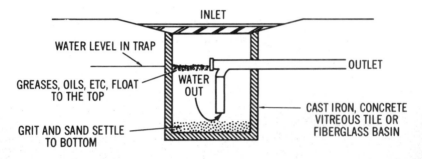

Fig. 2-3. A garage-type floor drain.

TRAPS

All traps must have a water seal of not less than 2 inches and not more than 4 inches. Special installations requiring a seal of more than 4 inches must be approved by the local authority. The purpose of a trap is to prevent sewer gas from entering a building through a drainage piping. Fig. 2-4 shows how water stops the passage of this sewer gas.

Most plumbing codes prohibit the use of certain types of traps. No trap that depends for its seal on the action of movable parts or concealed interior partitions shall be used. Full S traps, as shown in Fig. 2-5, are prohibited. No bell traps are permitted. Crown vented traps are prohibited. No fixture shall be double trapped.

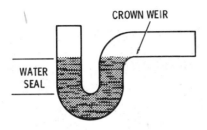

Fig. 2-4. A "P" trap. Traps should have a water seal of not less than 2 in. or more than 4 in.

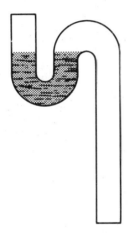

Fig. 2-5. An "S" trap. These traps are prohibited by almost all plumbing codes.

Drum traps are permitted only for *special* conditions or for use on fixtures which are specifically designed for drum traps. Where drum traps are permitted, they must be vented.

The common "P" and "S" traps are shown in Figs. 2-4 and 2-5, respectively. Another trap, illustrated in Fig. 2-6, is the plaster trap. Plaster traps are used in laboratories to catch materials that would clog the drainage piping. The water seal in the trap prevents the entrance of sewer gas.

35

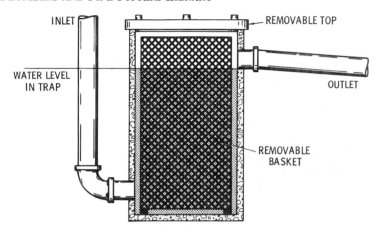

Fig. 2-6. Plaster trap.

Siphonage

In order to understand the operation of traps in general, one should first consider the principle of siphonage. The element of siphonage is a useful one in closet traps, but undesirable in fixture traps, and as will be later shown, provision must be made to prevent siphonage where undesirable. By definition, a siphon is *a bent pipe or tube, with legs of unequal length, used for drawing liquid out of a vessel by causing the liquid to rise within the tube, and over the rim or top.* The operation of a siphon, known as siphonage, and the effect of siphonage in breaking the seal in a trap, are shown in Fig. 2-7. From the illustration can be seen the necessity for providing a means of overcoming the tendency of the trap to empty whenever water is discharged from its fixture.

The effect of siphonage on unvented traps is shown in Fig. 2-7. Part *A* shows the normal state of the trap—full of water with the bowl empty. Part *B* shows the bowl full of water with an air space between the stopper and the trap water. In Part *C*, the stopper has been removed and the water is beginning to flow by gravity from the bowl; the space of air is being compressed. Part *D* shows the water flowing through the trap and out the drain pipe to the sewer. In Part *E*, the bowl and one leg of the trap is empty, with water still flowing out of the trap due to momentum and siphonage. In Part

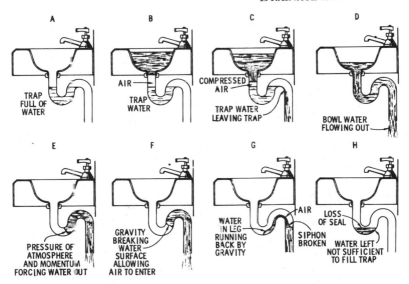

Fig. 2-7. The effect of siphonage on an S-type drain trap.

F, water is being siphoned out of the other leg of the trap, but the end surface of the water is breaking and dropping back to the bottom of the trap due to gravity. A solid column of water in the right leg of the trap, in Part *G,* is broken by gravity, allowing the air to enter and break the siphon. In Part *H,* the water remaining in the trap after breaking the siphon is not enough to retain the seal.

Toilet Bowl Traps

Toilet bowls are manufactured in four general types—the *siphon-jet,* the *blow-out,* the *reverse-trap,* and the *washdown.*

Siphon-Jet—The flushing action of the *siphon-jet* bowl (Fig. 2-8) is accomplished by directing a jet of water through the up leg of the trap to fill the trap and start the siphoning action instantaneously. The strong, quick, and relatively quiet action of the siphon-jet bowl, together with its deep water seal and large water surface, is universally recognized by sanitation authorities as one of the best types of toilet bowls. These outstanding features make the siphon-jet bowl suitable for the most exacting installations.

37

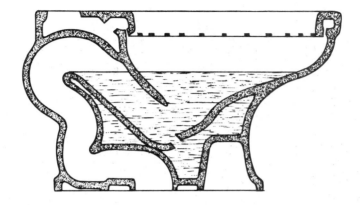

Fig. 2-8. A siphon-jet toilet bowl.

Blow-Out—The *blow-out* bowl (Fig. 2-9) cannot be fairly compared with any other type because it depends entirely on a driving jet action for its efficiency, rather than on siphoning action in the trap. It is economical in the use of water yet has a large water surface that reduces fouling space, a deep water seal, and a large unrestricted tap. Blow-out bowls are especially suited for use in schools, offices, and public buildings. They are operated with flush valves only.

Reverse-Trap—The flushing action and general appearance of the *reverse-trap* bowl (Fig. 2-10) is similar to the siphon-jet type.

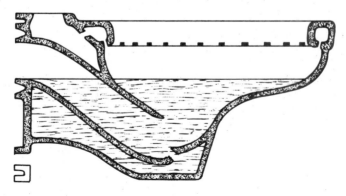

Fig. 2-9. A blow-out toilet bowl.

38

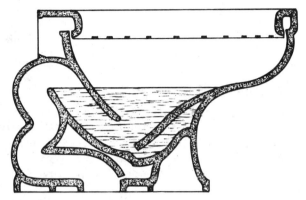

Fig. 2-10. A reverse-trap toilet bowl.

However, the water surface and size of the trap are smaller, and the depth of the seal is less, requiring less water for operation. Reverse-trap bowls are generally suitable for installation with either a flush valve or a low tank.

Washdown—The *washdown*-type bowl (Fig. 2-11) is simple in construction and yet highly efficient within its limitations. Washdowns are outlawed in many areas because a large area of the bowl is exposed to contamination. Proper functioning of the bowl is dependent on siphoning action in the trap, accelerated by the

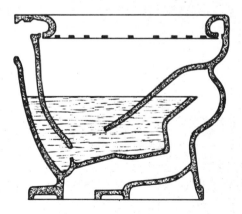

Fig. 2-11. A washdown toilet bowl.

39

force of water from the jet directed over the dam. Washdown bowls are widely used where low cost is a prime factor. They will operate efficiently with either a flush valve or a low tank.

Toilet Bowl Stoppages

Stoppages in toilet bowls are usually caused by foreign objects falling into the bowl. These obstructions can normally be cleared by using a force cup or, if necessary, a closet auger. If the stoppage is severe, and neither the force cup nor closet auger can remove the obstruction, it may be necessary to remove the bowl. To remove the toilet bowl, refer to Figs. 2-12 and 2-13, and proceed as follows:

1. Shut off the water and empty the flush tank by sponging.
2. Disconnect the water pipe from the tank.

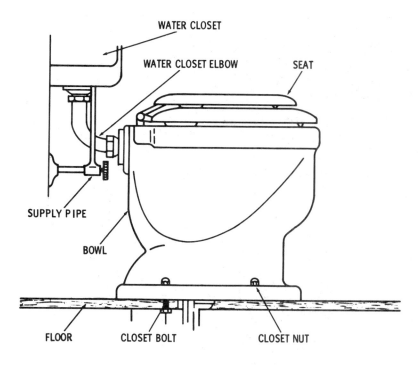

Fig. 2-12. Toilet bowl details.

GASKET

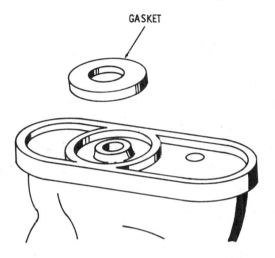

Fig. 2-13. View of typical toilet bowl base.

3. Remove the tank from the bowl if it is a two-piece unit, or disconnect the tank-bowl pipe connection if it is a wall-hung unit.
4. Remove the seat and cover from the bowl.
5. Remove the bolt covers from the base of the bowl and remove the bolts holding the bowl to the floor.
6. Break the seal at the bottom by jarring the bowl, and lift the bowl free.
7. Remove the obstruction from the discharge section.

To reinstall the toilet bowl, proceed as follows:

1. Obtain a wax seal or gasket from a plumbing supply house.
2. Clean the bottom of the bowl and place the wax seal or gasket around the bowl horn and press it into place (rocking it on the floor helps).
3. Set the bowl over the soil pipe and press it into place.
4. Install the floor-flange bolts, drawing them up snug. Do not overtighten (to do so may crack the base of the bowl). Use a level (carpenter's type preferred) when tightening the bolts to make sure the bowl is level, using shims if necessary.
5. Reinstall the items removed, including bolt covers, and water-pipe connections, seat, and cover.

41

DRAINAGE FITTINGS

A special fitting is used on drainage systems carrying liquid or water-carried wastes. The shoulders in the fittings are recessed to provide a smooth path for the waste material. Fig. 2-14 shows such a fitting. Drainage fittings are made in all the common fitting patterns, wyes, tees, and elbows.

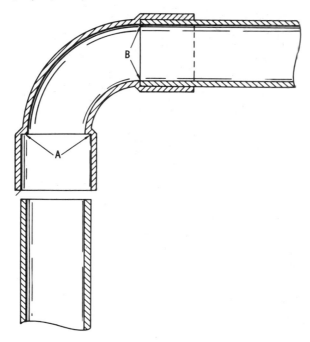

Fig. 2-14. A drainage fitting.

PROHIBITED FITTINGS AND PRACTICES

No double-hub fittings, single- or double-tapped tees, side inlet quarter bends, running threads, bands, or saddles should be used as a drainage fitting, except that a double-hub sanitary tapped tee may be used on a vertical line as a fixture connection.

No drainage or vent piping should be drilled and tapped for the purpose of making connections to the above.

No waste connection should be made to a closet bend or stub of a water closet or similar fixture.

There are other prohibited fittings and connections written into plumbing codes; the ones listed above are prohibited by most modern codes.

DEFINITIONS
(Taken from the Uniform Plumbing Code)

Branch—Any part of the piping system other than a main, riser, or stack.

Branch Vent—A vent connecting one or more individual vents with a vent stack or stack vent.

Building Drain—That part of the lowest piping of a drainage system which receives the discharge from soil, waste, and other drainage pipes inside the walls of the building and carries it to the building sewer.

Building Sewer—That part of the horizontal piping of a drainage system which extends from the end of the building drain and receives its discharge and carries it to a public sewer, private sewer, individual sewage-disposal system, or other point of disposal.

Circuit Vent—A branch vent that serves two or more traps and extends from in front of the last fixture of a horizontal branch to the vent stack.

Continuous Vent—A vertical vent that is a continuation of the drain to which it connects.

Developed Length—The developed length of a pipe is its length along the center line of the pipe and fittings.

Durham System—A term used to describe soil or waste systems where all pipe is of threaded pipe, tubing or other such rigid construction, using recessed drainage fittings to correspond to the types of piping.

Fixture Drain—The drain from the trap of a fixture to the junction of that drain with any other drain pipe.

Individual Vent—A pipe installed to vent a fixture trap and which connects with the vent system above the fixture served or terminates in the open air.

43

Loop Vent—Any vent connecting a horizontal branch or fixture drain with the stack vent of the originating waste or soil stack.

Plumbing Fixtures—Receptacles, devices, or appliances supplied with water or that receive liquid or liquid-borne wastes and discharge such wastes into the drainage system to which they may be directly or indirectly connected. Industrial or commercial tanks, vats, and similar processing equipment are not plumbing fixtures, but may be connected to or discharged into approved traps or plumbing fixtures when and as otherwise provided for in the plumbing code.

Sewage—Any liquid waste containing animal or vegetable matter in suspension or solution; may include liquids containing chemicals in solution.

Soil Pipe—Any pipe that carries the discharge of water closets, urinals, or fixtures having similar functions, with or without the discharge from other fixtures, to the building drain or building sewer.

Stack—The vertical main of a system of soil, waste, or vent piping extending through one or more stories.

Stack Vent—The extension of a soil or waste stack above the highest horizontal drain connected to the stack.

Trap—A fitting or device so designed and constructed as to provide, when properly vented, a liquid seal that will prevent the back passage of air without materially affecting the flow of sewage or waste water through it.

Trap Seal—The maximum vertical depth of liquid that a trap will retain, measured between the crown weir and the top of the dip of the trap.

Vent Stack—A vertical vent pipe installed primarily for the purpose of providing circulation of air to and from any part of the drainage system.

Vent System—A pipe or pipes installed to provide a flow of air to and from a drainage system or to provide a circulation of air within such system to protect trap seals from siphonage and back pressure.

Wet vent—A vent that also serves as a drain.

CHAPTER 3

Sewage Disposal

MUNICIPAL SEWAGE TREATMENT

Sewage treatment is much more aptly named *waste water treatment*. Waste water is actually 99.94 water by weight. Material suspended or dissolved in the water makes up the remaining .06 percent. Although sewage contains human wastes, it also contains all the waste matter and water discharged from homes, factories, processing plants of all kinds, gasoline service stations, garages or any other industry discharging wastes into the sewer system. There are three types of sewers:

1. Sanitary sewers carry liquid and water-borne wastes from homes, factories, and industrial and commercial facilities.
2. Storm sewers carry run-off water from streets, roofs, or other drainage not including human wastes.
3. Combination sewers are combined sanitary and storm sewers.

Waste water, after undergoing treatment, will eventually find its way into a river, lake, or other body of water (and in recent years its potential dangers have been recognized). The components of waste water that will deplete the oxygen supply of the stream, lake, or other body of water into which the treated waste water is discharged must be rendered harmless before the waste water effluent is discharged. Certain components of waste water effluent stimulate undesirable growth of plants or organisms and have an undesirable effect on downstream users of the water into which the effluent is discharged. Water contaminated with organic and inorganic materials is technically *polluted*.

The goal of a waste water treatment plant is to simulate as closely as possible the process by which nature cleans and purifies water. Contaminants that have been added to the water, such as phosphates, nitrates, other chemicals and disease-carrying germs must also be removed or neutralized. Human wastes and other organic matter are consumed, or digested by bacteria and other small organisms in water. The bacteria normally present in waste water must have oxygen to consume the raw sewage or other organic matter. A certain amount of dissolved oxygen (DO) is required by a body of water in order to stay alive. When an excessive amount of sewage is dumped into a body of water, the bacteria may use up all the available oxygen in the water in the digestive process. Without oxygen, fish and beneficial plant life die and the water becomes odorous. If the effluent or final discharge from a sewage treatment plant contains organisms that require a large amount of oxygen to aid further bacterial processing, the oxygen supply of the receiving body of water will be greatly depreciated. The measure of the amount of oxygen consumed in the biological process of breaking down organic matter in water is call BOD or *biological oxygen demand*. Therefore, the greater the degree of pollution, the higher becomes the BOD.

All the organics in waste water are not biologically degradable. Pesticides that cannot be broken down biologically may have adverse long-term effects and may contribute to odor, taste, and color problems in downstream water supplies. The COD (chemical oxygen demand) test is used to measure the quantities of nondegradable organics present in the waste water.

Pathogenic bacteria (bacteria that can transmit disease) and viruses are also present in waste water. If suspended solids are present in the final effluent from the treatment plant, the solids can shield the bacteria and virus from contact with disinfecting agents and thus slow down or prevent effective disinfection. Phosphorus and nitrogen, which are also present in waste water, may stimulate the growth of algae in the lakes or steams that receive the final effluent discharge. Algal growths may cause unpleasant taste and odor problems in downstream water supplies. Waste water treatment must be concerned with the removal of phosphorus and nitrogen.

The mineral quality of the potable water furnished by a water utility is changed during water usage. Calcium, sodium, magnesium, chlorides, sulfates, and phosphates are dissolved during water usage and become pollutants. These pollutants are called TDS (total dissolved solids). Control of the TDS present in the final effluent is important because the body of water that receives the final effluent from a treatment plant may be a supply source for a city further downstream.

Primary Waste Water Treatment

Primary waste water treatment is designed to remove both the pollutants that will settle—heavy suspended solids—and those that float, such as grease and oil. Primary treatment will not remove the dissolved pollutants; 60 percent of the raw sewage suspended solids and 35 percent of the BOD are removed in a typical primary process.

Secondary Treatment

Secondary treatment is designed to remove the soluble BOD left from the primary treatment and to remove more of the suspended solids. Secondary treatment does not remove any appreciable amount of phosphorus, nitrogen, COD, or heavy metals such as chromium, zinc, lead, silver, cadmium, and mercury. Pathogenic bacteria and viruses are not completely removed in the secondary treatment and may require further treatment before the final effluent is released into the receiving body of water.

Advanced Treatment

Advanced treatment may consist of allowing the final effluent of the secondary treatment plant to flow into irrigation systems serving soil crop acreages. Another method is to chemically treat and filter the final effluent—a process similar to the one used by a utility to process water. It is possible to remove as much as 99 percent of the BOD and phosphorus, all suspended solids and bacteria and 95 percent of the nitrogen, using some of these processes. The resulting water product is a clean, odorless, color-less, sparkling effluent, indistinguishable from drinking water.

Most of the impurities removed from waste water become "sludge," or suspended solids, in the process. The sludge may be further processed to serve as fertilizer, used as landfill, or incinerated.

SEQUENCE OF
WASTE WATER TREATMENT

Waste water processing or treatment is a combination of pro-cesses, both biological and physical, designed to remove organic matter from solution. This is the principle involved in sewage treatment ranging from the individual application, such as a septic tank or other home sewage treatment plant, to the large municipal treatment plants.

Municipalities must handle and treat millions of gallons of liquid and water carried wastes every day and dispose of the sludge and liquid effluent that are the end products of sewage treatment. The sludge can be treated and used as fertilizer, buried in a landfill, or incinerated. The liquid effluent must be chemically treated to kill any harmful bacteria that may remain after processing and then released into a filter bed, stream, river, or other body of water.

The block diagram shown in Fig. 3-1 illustrates the step-by-step process of treating sewage in one large midwestern municipality.

Sewage entering the treatment plant goes directly to a wet well. A bar screening device in the wet well picks out paper, rags, and other nonsoluble material for transmission to the incinerator. The remaining liquid wastes are lifted by a pump into the raw sewage tower. The raw sewage tower is designed to handle the maximum processing capacity of the treatment plant; any inflow of sewage in excess of the plant handling capacity is bypassed to a nearby creek. The raw sewage passing through the tower goes to the pre-aeration tank and grit chamber. Large blowers located in the

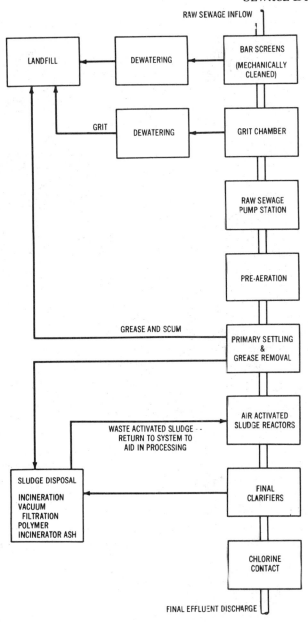

Fig. 3-1. Block diagram of sewage treatment process used by a large mid-western city.

49

blower room in the plant furnish air, which is circulated to jets located under water in the pre-aeration tank. The air, released under water in the tank, causes violent agitation of the water, breaking up the solids and separating the grit, sand, gravel, and glass from the fecal matter and greases. After a period in the pre-aeration and grit tank, the raw sewage travels to the primary settling tanks.

Primary Clarifiers

Raw waste water enters the circular primary settling tank through ports at the top of a central vertical inlet pipe. The inlet well directs the flow of liquid downward and equally in all directions. As shown in Fig. 3-2 the bottom of the tank is sloped to the center. A collector arm that rotates very slowly pushes the settled solids or sludge to the center of the tank where it is drawn off through the sludge draw-off well. A weir at the outside top edge of the tank permits outflow of liquid wastes only; floating solids drifting toward the edge of the tank are prevented from discharge by a baffle mounted in front of the weir. A skimmer mounted on the collector arm rotates with the collector arm and collects scum from the surface and deposits it into a scum box for transfer to the incinerator. The liquid effluent flowing over the weir is collected and piped to the air-activated sludge reactors.

Air-Activated Sludge Reactors

Air-activated sludge reactors are concrete tanks equipped with submerged air nozzles or diffusers designed for oxygenation and mixing of the liquid wastes entering the tank. Some of the activated sludge removed from the final settling tanks is recirculated to the activated sludge tank. The sludge, kept in suspension by air, forms contact material; dissolved and very fine organic matter is converted into activated sludge. The liquid waste (containing some sludge) now goes to the final settling tanks for clarification and chlorination.

Final Clarification

The liquid wastes move very slowly through the final settling tanks. Most of the material suspension in these tanks settles out as

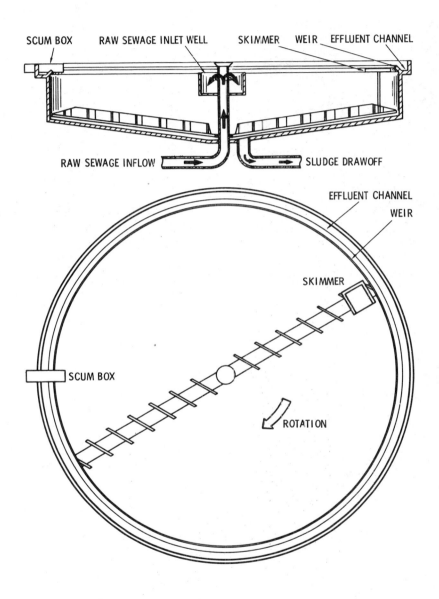

Fig. 3-2. Circular primary settling tank.

the liquid travels through. Chlorination of the effluent is the final step in treatment, and after sufficient contact time to ensure the satisfactory kill of the remaining organisms, the effluent is permitted to flow into a nearby creek.

As mentioned, part of the sludge removed from the final settling tanks is recirculated back to the air-activated sludge reactors; the remaining portion is piped to the incinerator site where it will be prepared for incineration.

Preparation for Incineration

When the sludge, which has been removed from the settling tanks, reaches the incinerator site, it is pumped into large circular tanks where it is mixed with ash from the incinerator. This process, called "thickening," is necessary in order for the sludge to be of the proper consistency when it reaches the vacuum filter.

Chemicals such as ferric chloride, lime, or polymers must be added to the thickened sludge to capture the fines which would otherwise be drawn through the filter medium. Polymers are often used because they are easier to feed into the thickened mixture and are often more economical. The polymers are added just before the vacuum filtration process begins.

Vacuum Filtration

The most common mechanical method used to de-water sludge in preparation for incineration is the use of rotary drum vacuum filtration. A cylindrical drum covered with a filter medium slowly rotates while partially submerged in a tank of thickened, chemically treated sludge. The filter medium, whether made of cloth or metal, is porous. As the drum is rotated slowly through the thickened sludge, vacuum is applied under the filter medium. The applied suction draws the sludge to the filter medium and holds it there; at the same time the suction also draws the water from the sludge. The extracted water is collected inside the drum and piped to a drain. As the drum rotates and reaches the release point for the sludge cake, the vacuum is broken and the sludge, now a semi-dry "cake," drops off, ready for final disposal. The filter medium continues to rotate, passing through a spray wash to prepare the filter for sludge pickup as the cycle continues. Vacuum filters are often installed in batteries, with the sludge cake dropping onto an endless belt conveyor and carried directly to the incinerators. A vacuum filter is shown in Fig. 3-3.

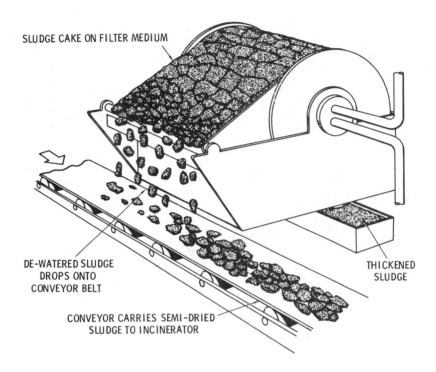

SLUDGE CAKE ON FILTER MEDIUM

DE-WATERED SLUDGE DROPS ONTO CONVEYOR BELT

THICKENED SLUDGE

CONVEYOR CARRIES SEMI-DRIED SLUDGE TO INCINERATOR

Fig. 3-3. A vacuum-type sludge filter.

Incinerators

Incineration of the sludge cake takes place in a multiple hearth furnace, similar to the one shown in Fig. 3-4. The furnace consists of a circular steel shell with several hearths in a vertical stack and a central rotating shaft with rabble arms. The sludge cake is fed into the top hearth, the rotating arms spread the cake and push it to the center where it drops to the second hearth. Here it is again spread and then pushed to the outside perimeter where it drops to the third hearth. The two upper-level hearths evaporate any remaining moisture from the sludge cake and the actual burning of the

53

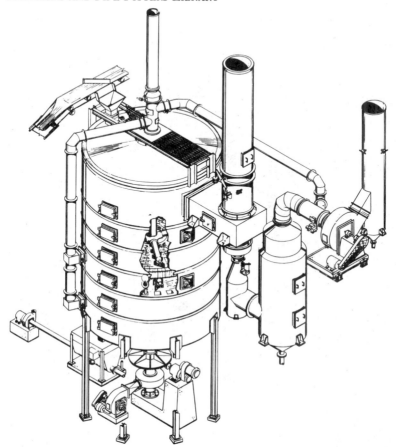

Fig. 3-4. A multiple-hearth

sludge starts at the third hearth. Subjected to temperatures between 1400° and 1500° F, the sludge is incinerated in the third and fourth hearths and the ash residue is cooled in the lower levels.

The smoke created in the process contains a high percentage of fly ash. This is removed by passing the smoke through a cyclonic wet scrubber before it is released to the atmosphere. The ash from the scrubber, combined with the ash from the incinerator, is mixed into a slurry and piped to the thickening tanks to be mixed with the incoming sludge.

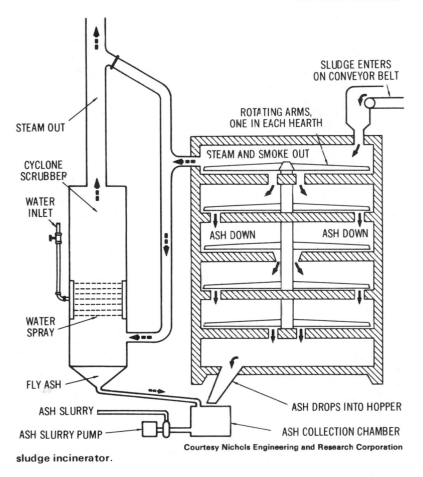

STEAM OUT

CYCLONE
SCRUBBER

WATER
INLET

WATER
SPRAY

FLY ASH

ASH SLURRY

ASH SLURRY PUMP

SLUDGE ENTERS
ON CONVEYOR BELT

ROTATING ARMS,
ONE IN EACH HEARTH

STEAM AND SMOKE OUT

ASH DOWN   ASH DOWN

ASH DROPS INTO HOPPER

ASH COLLECTION CHAMBER

Courtesy Nichols Engineering and Research Corporation

sludge incinerator.

INDIVIDUAL HOME
SEWAGE TREATMENT PLANTS

Individual home-sized sewage treatment plants use the same basic purification process as large central plants. Fig. 3-5 shows a cutaway view of a home-sized plant.

The *primary* treatment compartment receives the household sewage and holds it long enough to allow solid matter to settle to the sludge layer at the bottom of the tank. Organic solids are here broken down physically and biochemically by anaerobic bacteria (bacteria that live and work in the absence of oxygen). Grit and other untreatable materials are settled out and contained in the primary chamber. The partially broken down, finely divided material at the top of the primary compartment is passed on to the aeration chamber.

In the *aeration* chamber the finely divided, pretreated material from the primary compartment is mixed with activated sludge and aerated. Aerobic bacteria (bacteria that live and grow in the presence of oxygen) further digest the material which enters this chamber. Large quantities of air are injected into this compartment to hasten the digestive process. The aerobic bacteria use the oxygen in solution to break down the sewage and convert it into odorless liquids and gases. After treatment in this chamber, the liquid flows into the settling-clarifying compartment.

The final phase of the operation takes place in the *settling-clarifying* compartment. Here a tube settler eliminates currents and encourages the settling of any remaining settleable material, which is returned, by the sloping end wall in the tank, to the aeration chamber for further treatment. A nonmechanical surface skimmer, operated by hydraulics, skims any floating material from the surface of the settling compartment and returns it to the aeration chamber. The remaining odorless, clarified liquid flows into the final discharge piping through the baffled outlet.

If local health regulations require it, a nonmechanical chlorinator can be added to the plant to provide chemical sterilization of the effluent. If tertiary treatment is required, a separate up-flow filter providing further biological treatment from bacterial growth on the filter medium can be added. A chlorinator may also be added in the tertiary tank if desired. There are many areas where, due to soil composition, a septic tank and disposal field cannot provide a satisfactory solution to the problem of sewage disposal. The effluent from a septic tank requires further treatment by aerobic bacteria, in a finger system or a disposal field. If properly installed and maintained, a home-sized sewage treatment plant, such as is shown in Fig. 3-5, will produce an effluent that either reduces the requirements for subsurface filters (finger systems/disposal fields) or eliminates them entirely.

56

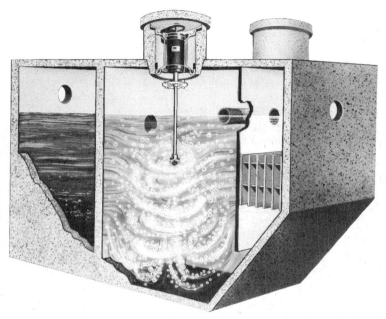

Courtesy Jet Aeration Co

Fig. 3-5. A home-sized sewage treatment plant.

SEPTIC TANKS

By definition, the word *septic* means any substance that produces or promotes decomposition of animal or vegetable matter. This process is regarded as a form of fermentation or breaking up of a complex organic compound into simpler compounds through the action of microorganisms called bacteria. Bacterial action is the basis of all septic tank systems. Waste from the kitchen, bathrooms, and laundry enter the subterranean septic tank. Through natural chemical processes, some of the mass is converted to gas, while the suspended solids settle to the bottom of the tank in the form of sludge.

The remaining liquid flows out of the tank through a series of conduits known as the disposal field. This field is provided with a

57

series of open-joint pipes laid in trenches that lead away from the tank and the house. By distribution through the field, the liquids are eventually absorbed by the soil. Soil conditions, the size of the house, and the number of occupants are among the determining factors for choosing the right size of tank and the proper disposal field. If the earth is composed of sand and gravel, and is consequently very absorbent, shorter fields will be satisfactory. If, however, there is clay present to impede absorption, the disposal field must be larger to accommodate the liquid to be absorbed.

The object of the tank is: (1) to provide a storage place where the motion of the liquid is arrested to give sufficient opportunity for the bacteria to reduce nearly all the solids to a liquid form, and (2) to provide a breeding place to increase the number of bacteria to accelerate the decomposition of the solids. The bacteria act strongly on the vegetable and animal solids, but cannot act on metal or mineral substances. This portion or sludge settles to the bottom of the tank and should be removed from time to time.

The bacteria begin their attack on the solids that settle to the bottom of the tank. During the process, gas is generated, and as the gas passes to the top of the liquid, it carries up with it particles of the solid matter, which collect at the surface of the tank, eventually forming a thick scum. This forms a breeding place for bacteria, thus augmenting the attacking force. Accordingly, there should be a large surface for scum to form to obtain maximum breeding of bacteria.

For favorable breeding conditions, the scum should remain as undisturbed as possible, and all air and light should be excluded. The sewage should remain in the tank long enough (about 24 hours) for the completion of the bacterial attack; that is, for the reduction of all the reducible solids to liquids. In order to meet the foregoing requirement in practice, the construction of the septic tank should provide:

1. A settling chamber to hold an undisturbed body of sewage to allow the solids to sink to the bottom where they are attacked, and to provide a scum surface for the breeding of bacteria which break down the solids.
2. Baffle boards, or turned-down elbows at the inlet and outlet of the settling chamber to prevent disturbance of the scum by

inflow and outflow of the settling chamber.
3. A watertight cover for protection and to exclude air and light, the condition favorable for maximum breeding of bacteria.

Tank Size

In order to provide satisfactory service, a septic tank should be large enough to hold the average amount of sewage discharged into it during a 24-hour period. Under no condition should the tank hold less than 500 gallons. The size of the house and the use of a garbage-disposal unit determine the necessary tank capacity. A two-bedroom home can be accommodated by a 500-gallon tank, while 600 gallons would be needed for three bedrooms, and 750 gallons for four bedrooms. Fifty percent extra capacity should be added to these figures if the house has a garbage-disposal unit, thus making the foregoing tank sizes 750, 900, and 1125 gallons, respectively.

Septic tanks are made of materials such as concrete, steel, vitrified clay, tile, and brick. They can be bought factory-built or can be constructed at the building site. They may contain single compartments or they may be of the two-chamber or multichamber variety. Two-chamber tanks are considered somewhat more efficient than single-compartment units. Tanks that are too small soon become overloaded with sludge and raw sewage, which then passes into the disposal field, clogging the system. A grease trap may or may not be necessary, depending on the size of the tank and local requirements.

Table 3-1 gives recommended tank sizes based on the number of people and the number of bedrooms in the house. Choose whichever size is the larger. For example, if there are six persons in the family, and the house has only two bedrooms, choose the 600-gallon tank. If, on the other hand, only four persons are served and the house has four bedrooms, choose the 750-gallon tank. This is a practical way of estimating the tank size that will be needed. It should be noted that these estimates are based on the number of persons living in the home for which the number of bedrooms are used as an index. Some authorities feels that a 1000-gallon tank should be the minimum for any new house, since with a tendency toward increased water consumption, the wastes will be propor-

Table 3-1. Septic-Tank Capacities

No. of bed- rooms in dwell- ing	Maxi- mum number persons served	Nominal liquid cap. in gallons	Recommended dimensions			
			Inside width	Inside length	Liquid depth	Total depth
2 or less	4	500	3 ft. 0 in.	6 ft. 0 in.	4 ft. 0 in.	5 ft. 0 in.
3	6	600	3 ft. 0 in.	7 ft. 0 in.	4 ft. 0 in.	5 ft. 0 in.
4	8	750	3 ft. 6 in.	7 ft. 6 in.	4 ft. 0 in.	5 ft. 0 in.
5	10	900	3 ft. 6 in.	8 ft. 6 in.	4 ft. 6 in.	5 ft. 6 in.
6	12	1,100	4 ft. 0 in.	8 ft. 6 in.	4 ft. 6 in.	5 ft. 6 in.
7	14	1,300	4 ft. 0 in.	10 ft. 0 in.	4 ft. 6 in.	5 ft. 6 in.
8	16	1,500	4 ft. 6 in.	10 ft. 0 in.	4 ft. 6 in.	5 ft. 6 in.

tionally larger. When domestic garbage grinders are installed or contemplated, the tank capacity shown in this table should be increased by 50 percent to provide additional sludge storage space.

Site Selection

When selecting a site for the septic tank, select ground that slopes away from the house. The tank may be located near the house, but if space is available, it is well to locate it 50 to 100 feet away from the house and at least 50 feet on the downhill side of the well. Many states require that the tank be at least 100 feet distant from a well. Its location and depth are often determined by the height of the lowest discharge in the house.

Construction

Built-on-site tanks are generally constructed in the manner shown in Fig. 3-6. After determination of the site, a hole is dug to such a depth that the tank inlet will line up with the house sewer. The length and width of the excavation should be made at least 1 ft. greater than the inside tank dimensions to provide space for the 6-in. concrete walls. Except in loose soils, the walls of the excavation can serve as the outside form if made straight and true. The inside-form construction for a 500-gal. tank is shown in Fig. 3-7.

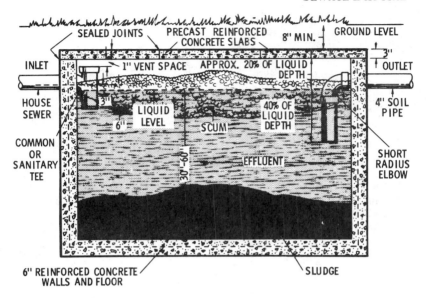

Fig. 3-6. Sectional view of a septic tank.

The corner assembly shown permits the end and side panels to be removed without damage. This is desirable when the form is to be reused.

Prior to moving the finished form into the hole, the outside faces should be mopped with oil or light grease to prevent the concrete from sticking. Metal-covered boxes on the end panels provide notches into which the inlet and outlet tees are mortared. The form is held in the correct position by spacer blocks about 6 in. long between the form faces and the walls of the excavation. These are removed as the concrete is placed. The floor is covered first with concrete to a thickness of 6 in. Placing the concrete in the walls should be started while the concrete in the floor is still soft, to ensure a water-tight bond, and should be continuous to avoid construction seams or joints. Concrete is distributed around the walls in layers of uniform depth so that the form will not be pushed out of position. The form is easily shoved out of place if one section of the wall is placed more rapidly than another. As the concrete is deposited, it is tamped and spaded along the form faces to obtain a dense, watertight wall. Care should be taken to

61

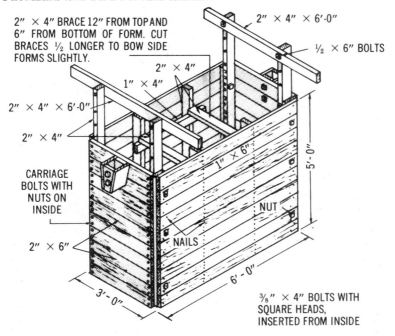

2" × 4" BRACE 12" FROM TOP AND
6" FROM BOTTOM OF FORM. CUT
BRACES ½ LONGER TO BOW SIDE
FORMS SLIGHTLY.

2" × 4" × 6'-0"

½ × 6" BOLTS

2" × 4"

1" × 4"

2" × 4" × 6'-0"

2" × 4"

CARRIAGE
BOLTS WITH
NUTS ON
INSIDE

1" × 6"

5' - 0"

NUT

2" × 6"

NAILS

3' - 0"

6' - 0"

⅜" × 4" BOLTS WITH
SQUARE HEADS,
INSERTED FROM INSIDE

Fig. 3-7. Form used for making a 500-gal. septic tank.

work the concrete around the boxes on the ends of the form. The top of the form should be stuck off carefully to provide a smooth, even support for the precast concrete slabs used for covers.

The form is removed after the concrete has hardened. If properly built and assembled, the forms should come off readily without damage. After the form is removed, and the inlet and outlet tees are mortared into the notches provided, the concrete is covered with burlap and kept wet. This aids in curing and increases the strength of the concrete. The cover sections can be cast on any level surface, provided the forms are properly built. The slabs are made 3 ½ in. thick, 12 in. wide, and long enough to reach across the tank. Each slab should be reinforced with three ⅜-in. round bars spaced 3 in. apart and placed about 1 in. above the bottom. Handles to facilitate handling, consisting of rings or bent reinforcing rods, can be embedded in the tops of the slabs while the concrete is still soft.

After the tank has been covered, the slabs are sealed with roofing cement to make the assembly watertight. When one or more of the slabs are removed to clean out the sludge in the tank, the joints should be carefully resealed after the slabs are replaced. Fig. 3-8 illustrates a cover slab with built-in cleanout pipes. Health authorities in some localities permit this type of cover slab.

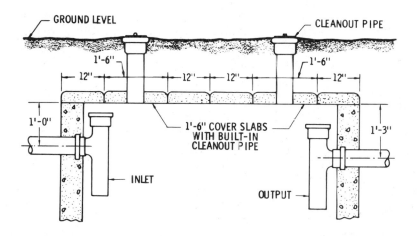

Fig. 3-8. Septic-tank cover slabs.

Prefabricated Septic Tanks

Iron, precast concrete, and vitrified-clay tanks can be purchased in many communities. These tanks are manufactured in various sizes in a central plant and are stockpiled ready for delivery on short notice. Iron tanks are rust-resisting and heavily coated with a preservative, and although opinion differs as to their permanence, some authorities claim that a 12-gauge tank will last 10 to 15 years. Concrete and vitrified-clay tanks, on the other hand, should last indefinitely if properly constructed.

Since baffle boards, inlet, outlet, and cleanout connections are usually built into the tanks, installation requires only lowering the tank from the delivery truck into the prepared excavation. The various connections to the tank are then performed in the usual way. Prefabricated tanks are made in various shapes, so that the

63

dimensions may differ somewhat from those shown in Table 3-1. The total tank capacity and the depth of the liquid are the two most important considerations.

GREASE TRAPS

When grease traps are installed as a part of the sewage-disposal system, they may be provided for as shown in Fig. 3-9. The reason for placing the grease trap or grease basin separately from the house sewer is that no running traps should be placed in the house sewer because they might become obstructed to prevent free movement of air through the sewer and soil stack. As noted in Fig. 3-9, a grease trap is a small tank into which the kitchen waste

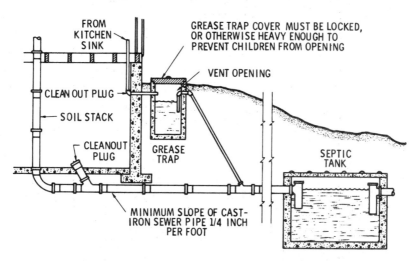

Fig. 3-9. A grease-trap arrangement and the method of connecting to a septic tank.

empties before it enters the main sewer line. Since grease is lighter than water, it collects at the top, and the water is drained off from the bottom of the tank. In order to be of service, however, the grease must be removed before it fills the trap, for when the trap is full, the grease will continue into the sewer, thus completely eliminating the trap's value.

Grease traps may be built of concrete or masonry, using the same construction principles as those previously described for septic tanks. The trap should be installed just outside the house and as near the kitchen as possible. The size depends on the amount of kitchen waste, but if used in connection with a garbage-disposal unit, a size of about 100 gal. will be necessary.

HOUSE SEWER

The septic tank is connected to the house drain by a line of pipe called a house sewer or sewer pipe. The house sewer is a very important part of the plumbing system and is the main highway for all the wastes from the numerous drains and soil stacks. It is usually built of 6-in. hub-and-spigot sewer pipe.

Sewer Joints

In connecting the house sewer with the septic tank, all joints should be thoroughly filled with a mixture of one part cement, three parts mortar mix, and enough water to make a plastic consistency. When properly made, such joints will normally keep out roots. Sometimes, as a further precaution against root penetration, a mortar band 1 in. thick and 3 in. wide is made around the joint.

Any mortar squeezed out on the inside of the pipe and left there might cause clogging. Therefore, after each section is laid, the inside joints should be wiped smooth with a swab. Hub-and-spigot sewer pipe can be purchased with a coating of composition material which seals the joints on contact. This material replaces the mortar joints and prevents roots from clogging the sewer line. Cast iron sewer pipe is used for the sewer line when it is less than 3 ft. under a driveway, within 50 ft. of a well or suction line, within 10 ft. of any drinking-water supply line under pressure, or within 5 ft. of basement walls.

Slope

The recommended slope for both house drain and house sewer is 1 in. in 4 ft. toward the septic tank. When it is necessary to give the house sewer more slope than this per foot, about 10 ft. of the line next to the tank is leveled off to slope 1 in. in 4 ft. This will assist in reducing the rate of flow of sewage to the tank.

Cleanouts

Whenever possible, the house sewer should be laid without bends or change in slope, which could result in clogging. When, however, the site does not allow a straight sewer, cleanouts should be provided at each bend of more than 45° and at each change in fall of more than 22½°. The cleanout may be made from a tee-section sewer pipe inserted in the line with a leg extending to ground level. Then, in case of clogging at this point, a rod can be inserted in the leg to remove any lodged material. The top of the cleanout pipe should be kept tightly covered with a brass or concrete cap. A cleanout pipe is sometimes installed in the sewer line just before it enters the tank, since clogging will at times occur at this point.

Outlet Sewer

The septic tank is connected to a distribution box with a line of pipe termed the *outlet sewer.* This line is usually built of 4-in. hub-and-spigot sewer pipe with the joints well mortared. The precautions pertaining to bends, root-proofing, and watertight construction governing house-sewer installation also apply to the outlet sewer. The recommended slope for the outlet sewer to the distribution box is 1 in. in 25 ft.

DISTRIBUTION BOX

The distribution box is an integral part of any well-planned sewage disposal system, and distributes the liquids from the septic tank to the disposal lines. This box helps equalize the flow into the disposal lines and permits inspection of the sewage liquids. The distribution box may be made circular or rectangular, although the rectangular type is recommended when three or more disposal-line outlets are required. Since the distribution box should distribute the liquid evenly in the outlet lines, care should be taken to have all the outlets on the same horizontal level.

The box size should be in some proportion to the septic tank size, but should always be at least 18 in. wide and long enough to accommodate the required number of outlet pipes, allowing 9 in. of box length for each outlet. The same construction principles as that employed on septic tanks should be adhered to, although only 4-in. walls and bottom are required for the average size distribution box. An inner form is constructed after excavation, being made with 1-in. sheathing and 2 × 4 studs. The concrete floor and walls are usually placed in one continuous operation. The cover can be of several precast slabs or one large slab, depending on the size of the box.

Prefabricated distribution boxes can usually be obtained from septic tank manufacturers in sizes to suit individual requirements. The tile or concrete pipe connection between the septic tank and distribution box should be at least 4 in. in diameter, with the length to suit the local conditions, such as the available area for the disposal field, the amount of discharge sewage and the size of the septic tank. In all other respects, the installation should be performed in the same manner as that described for the house-sewer connection.

PERCOLATION TEST

To estimate the size and location of the disposal field, the home-owner is advised to ascertain the absorption properties of the soil. This is known as the percolation test, and consists of digging several holes at various locations on the contemplated disposal field and filling them with water overnight. After they have dried, the holes are again filled and a record is made of the time it takes the water to seep away.

If the water drops 1 in. in 2 minutes or less, it indicates a need for 85 sq. ft. of trench bottom for each bedroom in the house. If the 1-in. drop takes 10 to 50 minutes it means that 165 sq. ft. is required for each bedroom. If more than 1 hour is needed to lower the water line by 1 in., the ground is not suitable for a shallow absorption disposal system.

THE DISPOSAL FIELD

The final stage of sewage disposal is accomplished in the disposal field, since the duty performed by the septic tank consists
principally in the reduction of the solid matter originally contained
in the raw sewage. This operation is important, however, as without it further purification would be a difficult matter. The discharge from a septic tank contains much organic matter in solution, which must be changed into oxides and nitrogen compounds,
and this final process of purification depends on the action of an
entirely different class of bacteria than those which breed in septic
tanks.

The bacteria necessary for the final stages of purification are to
be found near the surface of the earth; hence subsurface systems
are usually employed. The disposal field shown in Fig. 3-10 consists of two or more lines of drain tile laid with open joints in
specially prepared trenches. The sewage liquid flows from the
distribution box into the tile lines, where it seeps out through the
open joints into the gravel fill. Here it is worked on by bacteria,
which complete the disposal process. Since these types of bacteria
require air, it is advisable to provide a porous bed, such as gravel
or crushed stone, in the trench in which the bacteria can do their
work most effectively. Some soils are sufficiently open and porous
so that special fills are not needed around the tiles. It should be
remembered, however, that sewage is not necessarily rendered
harmless in the disposal field; therefore, precautions should be
taken to observe certain minimum distances between the disposal
field and water-supply systems.

It should also be kept in mind that a disposal field must have
adequate capacity to take care of the sewage. The length of the
disposal lines required depends on the absorption qualities of the
soil. Trenches more than 100 ft. in length should not be used. At
least two disposal lines should be installed, even though less than
100 ft. of disposal line are required. Then, if one of the lines should
become temporarily waterlogged, the other line can still function.
The disposal lines may be laid to form a closed loop on fairly level
ground, as in Fig. 3-11, but the disposal lines should be laid as in
Fig. 3-10 to follow the contour on a hillside.

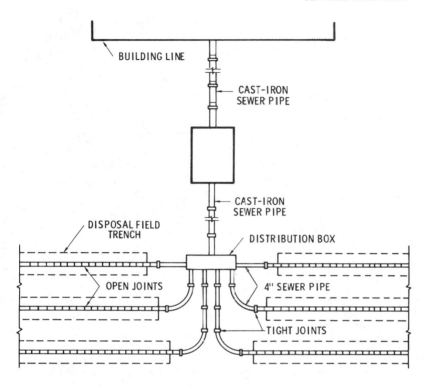

Fig. 3-10. Layout of a typical disposal field.

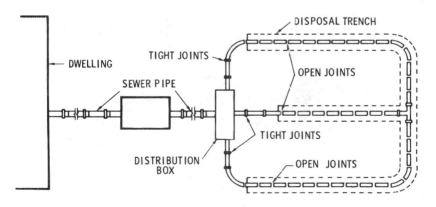

Fig. 3-11. Layout of a typical closed-loop disposal field.

69

A sealed discharge line, about 6 to 8 ft. in length, should connect each disposal tile line with the distribution box. This watertight connection helps in keeping the area around the distribution box from becoming waterlogged. The remainder of each disposal line consists of 4-in. drain tile laid with ¼- to ½-in. joint openings and with a slope of 2 to 4 in. per 100 ft.

To obtain a true, uniform slope, the tile is often laid on a grade board, as illustrated in Fig. 3-12. Where feasible, the depth of the tile line below ground should average about 18 in. Gravel, crushed stone, or cinders are placed around and over the tile line to provide a porous liquid-absorbing bed. A layer of untreated building paper is finally placed over the porous material to prevent the loose earth backfill from clogging the bed. The open-joint pipes of the disposal field should be laid in trenches 18 to 36 in. wide and an equal distance in depth.

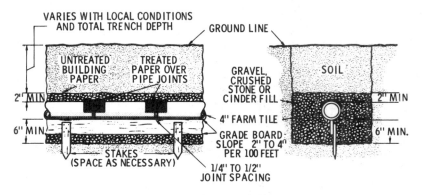

(A) Trench in clay soil.

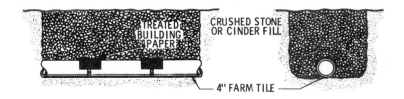

(B) Trench layouts for various soil conditions.

Fig. 3-12. Trench layouts for various soil conditions.

70

CHEMICAL PRECIPITATION

By the addition of certain chemicals to the sewage, chemical action is set up that greatly increases the rapidity with which precipitation takes place. The best chemical to use depends on the sewage, local conditions, and local law. When used, the chemical should be added to the sewage and thoroughly mixed before it reaches the distribution box.

SIPHON ACTION

When used in a sewage-disposal system, the purpose of a siphon tank is to secure an intermittent discharge, thus allowing a considerable period of time for one sewage dose to work off in the soil spacer before another flush is received. It also provides distribution over a larger area and in a more even manner than if the sewage were allowed to dribble with an uncontrolled flow.

The siphon action is rather simple and requires two conditions for its operation:

1. All air must be evacuated from the piping.
2. The discharge end must be lower than the liquid level in the tank from which the liquid is to be removed.

This action may best be illustrated with reference to Fig. 3-13 in which is shown a siphon consisting of a partly-filled liquid container and an inverted U-tube. When the foregoing conditions exist, the liquid length *(A)* in the long leg is heavier than the liquid length *(B)* in the short leg, resulting in a discharge through the long leg. The discharge tends to create a vacuum at *C* which permits atmospheric pressure to force liquid from the container up the short leg, and over into *A* to replace the discharged liquid. When the liquid level *(B)* in the container has been lowered until it is equal to the level *A*, the flow will automatically stop. It should be noted that the level *(B)* should never fall below the end of the short tube, which will stop the siphon action so that it will not restart.

The siphon action is also used occasionally for the discharge of liquid from tanks, and to obtain water from a hillside, well, or

71

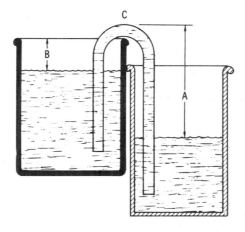

Fig. 3-13. Liquid transfer by means of siphon action.

spring from which water can flow by gravity. In such instances, the surface of the water may be near enough to the ground surface to take advantage of the gravity all the way. If, however, the surface of the water is some distance from the ground surface (less than 20 ft.), a siphon can be used to lift the water over the top for delivery to a point below the upper water level. All that is required is that the point of discharge be lower than the water level at the source.

SEWAGE SIPHONS

As previously noted, sewage siphons are sometimes employed to facilitate sewage disposal when septic tanks are used. It should be clearly noted that a siphon, in order to function properly, must be installed in the distribution carrier; that is, in the sewer connected to the distribution field. Fig. 3-14 shows three types of sewage siphons. The essential principles of operation are the same in all—a column of air is trapped between two columns of water, and when the water in the tank rises to a predetermined height (called the discharge line), the pressure forces out the confined air, upsetting the balance and causing a rush of water through to the

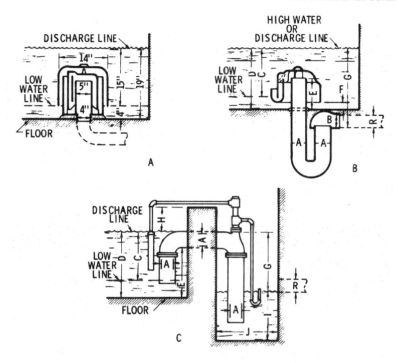

Fig. 3-14. Three types of sewage siphons.

pipes leading to the distribution field. The entire operation is fully automatic and occurs as a function of the water level in the tank.

The siphons shown in Fig. 3-14 are commercial products and are made of cast iron. Manufacturers of sewage siphons usually furnish full information for their setting and other details. To put a siphon such as that shown in Fig. 3-14B in service, all that is required is to set the siphon trap (U-shaped pipe) plumb with respect to the tank, making the height *(E)* from the floor to the top of the long leg as specified. Next, fill the siphon trap with water until it begins to overflow at *B*, and place the bell in position. The siphon is now ready for service. Do not fill the vent pipe on the side of the bell. An overhead siphon, such as that shown in Fig. 3-14C, operates in a similar manner and may be installed in a tank already built by the addition of an outlet pump.

73

Figs. 3-15 and 3-16 serve to illustrate typical siphon installations in two-chamber septic tanks. The dimensions of the tanks should conform with modern practice, with a capacity sufficient to hold the average amount of sewage discharged into it during a 24-hour

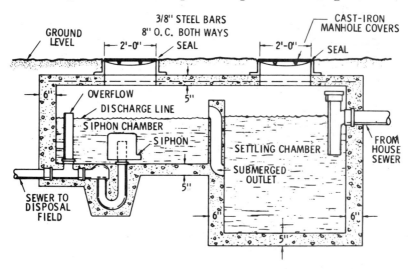

Fig. 3-15. One type of two-chamber septic tank equipped with a siphon.

period. If properly installed and maintained, sewage siphons require very little attention and will flush without failure for many years. In common with other plumbing fixtures, however, they are susceptible to stoppage if rags, newspapers, and similar solids get into the sewage. Also, when fouling of the sniffling hole or vent prevents the entrance of sufficient air into the bell, the siphon action will stop until the siphon is thoroughly cleaned. It is well to remember that siphons are for handling liquid only, and if sludge is allowed to accumulate, it will prevent their proper operation until the sludge is removed.

TANK SIZE CALCULATIONS

Problem—It is desired to build a circular septic tank having a nominal liquid capacity of 750 gal. Calculate the inside dimensions of the tank when the liquid depth is not to exceed 4 ft.

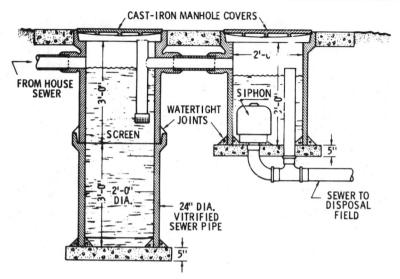

Fig. 3-16. A dual-chamber septic tank with siphon.

Solution—The foregoing may easily be calculated if it is remembered that the volume for a cylinder equals the bottom area multiplied by the height. Since the area of the bottom equals $(\pi D^2 \div 4)$, then $(\pi D^2 \div 4)h$ equals the volume in cubic feet. Since 750 gal. equals approximately 100 cu. ft., our equation becomes:

$$\frac{3.14D^2}{4}$$

Solving for the inside tank diameter D;

$$3.14D^2 = 100, \text{ or } D = \sqrt{\frac{100}{3.14}} = 5.645 \text{ ft.}$$

The inside tank diameter required is approximately 5 ft. 8 in. Assuming that the tank is required to be an additional foot in height, the required inside height will be 5 ft.

Problem—A four-bedroom dwelling requires a 1200-gal. septic tank. If the floor of the tank is 4½ ft. by 7½ ft., calculate the liquid depth and total depth of the tank.

75

Solution—Since the cubical content of the liquid equals approximately 1200 ÷ 7.5, or 160 cu. ft., the depth of the contents will obviously be 160 ÷ 4.5 × 7.5, or 4.74 ft., which is approximately 4 ft. 9 in. From the foregoing, it follows that the inside dimensions of the tank will be: inside width 4 ft. 6 in.; inside length 7 ft. 6 in.; liquid depth 4 ft. 9 in.; total depth 5 ft. 9 in.

Problem—The absorption properties of the soil for a certain disposal field are such that 100 sq. ft. are required for each bedroom in a four-bedroom home. Assuming a nominal liquid capacity of the septic tank at 750 gal., what will be the total area and length of the field when each of four open-joint drain pipes are placed 36 in. apart?

Solution—Since the four drain pipes are spaced 3 ft. apart, the total width occupied by the trenches is 4 × 3, or 12 ft. The total length of the 400-sq. ft. field will therefore be 400 ÷ 12, or 33 ft. 4 in.

SEPTIC-TANK MAINTENANCE

To give maximum protection and trouble-free sewage disposal, even the most carefully planned and constructed sewage disposal system requires occasional maintenance. For example, as a result of the chemical action taking place in the septic tank, a layer of sludge gradually accumulates on the bottom of the tank and scum collects on the top, both of which reduce the space required for the liquids.

Sludge and scum should not be permitted to accumulate to a combined depth of more than approximately 18 in. If the septic tank is properly installed, it should operate for several years without the need of cleaning. A check should be made at the distribution box every two or three years to determine the condition of the tank. If sludge appears in the distribution box, the septic tank needs attention. Cleaning can be accomplished with the aid of a pump or long-handled scoop. Because sludge often carries disease germs, it should be promptly buried. Occasional inspection should also be made of the tile lines in the disposal field to see that settlements in the tile trench do not affect the original alignment of the individual tiles.

CHAPTER 4

Soldering

By definition, *soldering* is the act or process of forming joints upon or between metallic surfaces by means of a fusible alloy or solder whose melting point is lower than that of the metals to be united. Briefly, the process is as follows: After carefully cleaning the joint, a *flux* is applied to the cleaned areas to prevent oxidation, and a suitable quantity of solder is fused on the joint by a pressure flame.

Soldering is sometimes confused with welding. A solder joint is a *laminated* joint. A welded joint is a *fused* joint; that is, the metals are actually melted together to form one integral piece.

Hard, or so-called silver solder, used by plumbers and pipe fitters, is an alloy, made in several different grades and sold under various trade names.

SWEATING COPPER TUBING

There are a few simple rules to follow when sweating (solder-ing) copper tubing joints. If you learn and follow these rules, you can make perfect sweat joints every time.

1. The male end of the tubing and the female end of the fitting must be clean and bright.
2. The piping being joined *must* be dry. It is impossible to sweat a joint properly if there is water in the joint.
3. Use plain 50/50 or 95/5 solder, whichever is best for the particular job, and a noncorrosive soldering paste flux. Do not use acid core or rosin core solder.
4. Heat must be applied to the right place on the fitting. Capil-lary action will then pull the solder into the joint.
5. When working on a closed system of piping (i.e., one in which the piping being connected is closed by a valve or other fitting at the ends), a valve or fitting must be opened. When heat is applied to a closed system of piping, pressure is built up. If the built-up pressure is not relieved, it will cause the melted solder to blow out of the newly made joint and cause a leak.

Clean the male ends of the copper tubing and the female ends of the fitting with sand cloth or fitting brush. Coat the cleaned ends with solder paste. Join the pieces together and apply heat from the torch. Fig. 4-1 shows where the heat should be applied. Apply the end of the solder to the joint; when the joint is at the right tempera-ture for sweating, the solder will flow into the joint. Play the heat from the torch all around the fitting as shown in Fig. 4-1. Follow the heat around with the solder, making sure that the solder has flowed into the joint all the way around. Remove the heat and allow the joint to cool.

CUTTING COPPER TUBING

The best tool to use for cutting copper tubing is the type shown in Fig. 4-2. This cutter is available for tubing sizes from ⅛ in.

through 4 in. The burr left on the inside of the tubing should be reamed out after the cut is made.

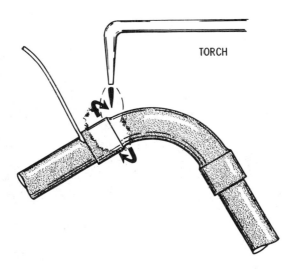

Fig. 4-1. Sweating (soldering) copper pipe and fittings. Heat should be applied on the back side of the fitting to draw the solder into the joint.

SOLDER-JOINT VALVES

Plumbing, heating, and air-conditioning systems require sturdy valves with resistant features. *Kennedy* valves, with cylindrical-shaped bodies, have excellent distortion-resisting qualities, and the stem design assures maximum resistance to the common cause of stem failure. Solder-joint valves have threadless, smooth pipe ends into which standard types of copper tubing can be fitted. At the inner end of the socket, a square shoulder acts as a stop, which limits pipe insertion (see Fig. 4-3).

Caution: The safe working pressure-temperature ratings for a soldered piping system depend not only on the valves and tube strength but also on the composition of the solder used for joints. Do not use a solder-joint valve on lines carrying flammable gases or liquids. In the event of fire, heat might melt the solder joint,

79

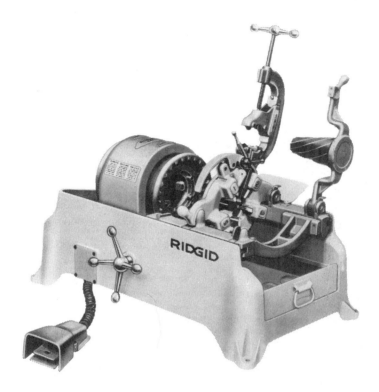

Fig. 4-2. A cutter used to cut copper tubing.

Fig. 4-3. A typical solder-end bronze gate valve.

releasing the liquid or gas as additional fuel for the flames. Also, a pipe fitter attempting to dismantle a solder joint on a gas line by melting out the joints might cause a fire or explosion from the residue of oil or gas in the line.

When solder-joint valves are installed, the type of solder used must be suitable for the service pressure and temperature. Solder-joint valves must be open when installed.

CHAPTER 5

Lead Work

Lead has virtually vanished from the plumbing scene in most areas of the country. Today, its main use is making lead bends for toilets. Nevertheless, knowing how to make a wiped joint—one in which lead or other sections are soldered together—is still required in many examinations for plumbing licenses. Hence, what follows is a detailed description of how to make a wiped joint. If you do have the occasion to work with lead, it will be well to observe the precautions for handling it that were outlined in Volume 2 of this series.

JUDGING THE SOLDER

A requirement in lead work is the ability to judge the quality of solder. The plumber must know by its appearance when it contains the right proportions of lead and tin. To preserve these proportions, it is necessary to keep the solder from overheating, because in overheating, some of the tin will burn, thus destroying the correct proportions. The tin burns because its melting point is lower than that of the lead. The quality of the solder may be judged by pouring out a small quantity on a brick or stone and noting the color when it sets, and the number and size of bright spots on its surface. When the proportions are correct, there will appear on a test sample (almost the size of a half dollar) three or four small bright spots. The side of the solder next to the brick will be bright. Adding lead will reduce the size and number of spots; adding tin will increase them. Thoroughly stir the solder before pouring out a test sample. The rate of cooling affects the appearance of the test sample; if cooled too quickly, the solder will appear *finer* than it really is.

When the tin burns, it is indicated by the formation of dross on the surface, specks of which turn bright red and smoke. Too little tin in the solder will cause the solder to melt the lead pipe on which it is poured; it will burn the tinning of a brass ferrule or union and set free zinc from the brass, which will mix with the solder and render it unfit for joint wiping. The right heat of the solder is judged by the color or bloom on the surface of the molten solder, or by holding the ladle near the face. An easier test for the beginner is to stir with a wooden stick; when it is at the right temperature it will char the stick; if it is too hot, the stick will burn.

PROPORTIONING THE SOLDER

Wiping solder is composed of two parts lead and one part tin. In using wiping solder, the numerous heatings and occasional over-heatings will result in loss of some of the tin content. It is necessary to add a little tin from time to time to restore the proper balance of lead and tin. Since tin is lighter than lead, it tends to float on top of the lead, and unless the wiping solder is stirred before a ladleful is removed, an excess amount of tin will be removed. Table 5-1. shows the properties of lead and tin.

The following method of making wiping solder is recommended: Melt down 20 lbs. of lead and 10 lbs. of tin, using a new or clean lead pot. When the lead and tin have melted, throw in 2 oz. of rosin, and stir well. When heated to 600° the wiping solder is ready

Table 5-1. Properties of Lead and Tin

Ingredients	Melting Point	Specific Gravity	Weight	
			Per cu. in.	Per cu. ft.
Lead	620°F	11.07 to 11.44	.4106	709.7
Tin	449°F	7.297 to 7.409	.2652	458.3

for use. A piece of newspaper submerged in the solder will ignite at 600°.

PREPARING JOINT FOR WIPING

It is important that the ends of the lead pipes to be joined are properly treated before wiping. The two essential requirements for a satisfactory flow of liquid through the pipe in service are as follows:

1. That the ends of the pipes to be joined properly fit, so that in pouring the solder, it will not run through the joint and form an obstruction.
2. That there are no sharp internal projections at the joint that would catch lint or any other foreign matter.

In addition, the formation given to the ends of the pipes should be such as to form a socket into which the solder will flow, thus making the joint stronger than if merely built up around the outer surfaces of the two pipes.

The operations to be performed in preparing the joint for wiping consist of :

1. Squaring.
2. Removing burrs.
3. Flaring the female end.
4. Rasping the outer edge.
5. Pointing the male end.
6. Soiling.
7. Marking.
8. Shaving.
9. Setting.

Various tools are used in performing these operations.

85

To secure a good fitting joint, so that when the solder is poured it will not run inside the pipes, the ends of the pipe must first be squared, as shown in Fig. 5-1. Cut the pipe as true as possible. The skilled workman will be able to judge when the end is square by eye, but the beginner should use a try square to test the trueness of the end. When the pipe is cut, especially if a wheel cutter is used (such as shown in Fig. 5-2), burrs will be formed on the inside and outside of the pipe. At this stage, the inside burr should be removed by using a reamer, tap borer, or a shave hook, as shown in Fig. 5-3.

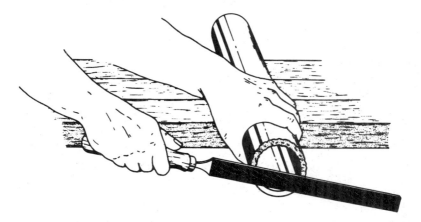

Fig. 5-1. Preparing a joint for wiping by squaring the end.

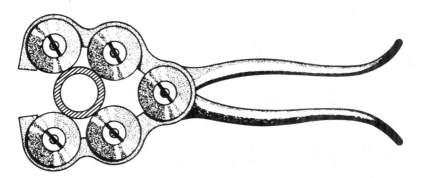

Fig. 5-2. Wheel lead-pipe cutter.

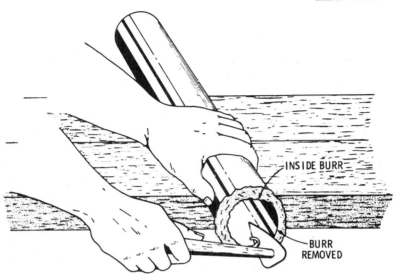

INSIDE BURR

BURR REMOVED

Fig. 5-3. Removing burrs from end of pipe.

In the further preparation of the ends, the *female end* is flared or belled out with a *turn pin* as shown in Fig. 5-4. The pipe is flared so that the end is enlarged about a quarter of an inch. The result is shown in Fig. 5-5. After flaring, the outer burrs should be removed with a rasp, holding it in a plane parallel to the surface of the pipe as shown in Fig. 5-6. This is done to reduce the amount of solder necessary in wiping. The next step is to *point* the *male end* with a rasp, as shown in Fig. 5-7. The taper on this end should be somewhat longer than on the other end to permit sweating, which is desirable as it increases the strength of the joint. This is shown in the enlarged section in Fig. 5-8. In pointing, the fit of the two ends should be frequently tested until the fit shown in Fig. 5-8 is approximated. The ends are now ready for soiling.

First, remove all grease or oil from the pipe by rubbing the surface with chalk, sand, or wire cloth, thus presenting a clean surface to which the soil will adhere. The soil is a composition of lamp black mixed with a little glue and water; it is painted around the pipe (as shown in Fig. 5-9) to prevent the adhesion of the melted solder except at its proper place, thus giving a neat and finished appearance. Ready-mixed plumbers' soil may also be

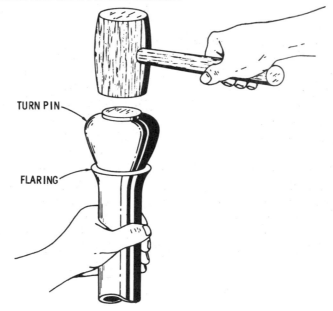

Fig. 5-4. Flaring female end of pipe.

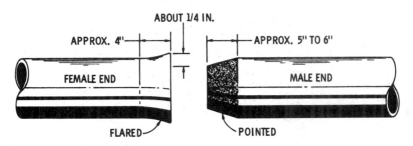

Fig. 5-5. Shape of female and male ends of pipe.

obtained. In the absence of the prepared article, use old-fashioned shoe blacking; this, however, is not as satisfactory as regular soil. To make the soil, take ½ oz. of pulverized glue and dissolve it in water, and gradually add a pint of dry lamp black with water enough to bring it to the consistency of cream. Boil and stir until the glue is thoroughly incorporated with the black. This will have to be done slowly, and when it has progressed far enough, test it as

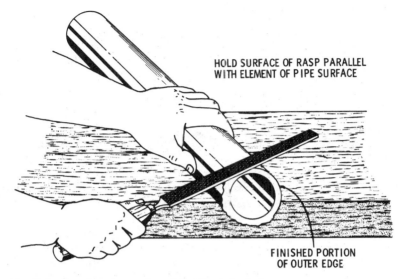

HOLD SURFACE OF RASP PARALLEL
WITH ELEMENT OF PIPE SURFACE

FINISHED PORTION
OF OUTER EDGE

Fig. 5-6. Rasping outer edge of female end of pipe.

Fig. 5-7. Pointing the male end of pipe.

89

follows: Paint a little of the soil on a piece of pipe, and when dry, rub it smartly with your finger. If it comes off easily, add more glue, but if it sticks and takes a slight polish, it is good. If it curls off when heat is applied, there is too much glue in it, or the pipe was not cleaned prior to applying.

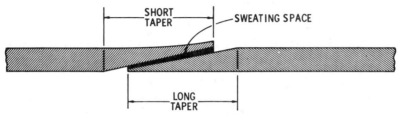

Fig. 5-8. Enlarged section of the male and female pipe.

The entire end of each pipe is painted, with the soil extending beyond the joint limit as shown in Fig. 5-9. For neatness, paint the outer soil limit (on both pipes) to the lines by wrapping a piece of paper or cardboard around the pipe with the edge at the desired outer soil limit. After the soil dries, the excess must be removed from the pipe end up to the inner soil limit, which governs the length of the joint or the distance along the pipe to which the solder will adhere. The pipe ends are now ready for *shaving*. This consists of removing the soil between the pipe end and the inner soil limit to order to obtain a clean bright surface to which the solder will adhere. Both the internal and external surfaces must be shaved

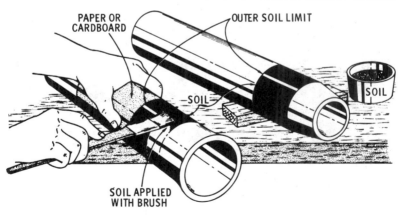

Fig. 5-9. Applying the soil to pipe.

90

so that all the surface that comes in contact with the solder will be bright; otherwise the solder will not adhere.

Immediately after shaving, apply a little tallow to the shaved surfaces to preserve them from the oxidizing action of the atmosphere, which would otherwise tarnish the surface and form a film to which the solder will not adhere. The pipes are now ready for the final preparatory operation of setting. They have the appearance shown in Fig. 5-10.

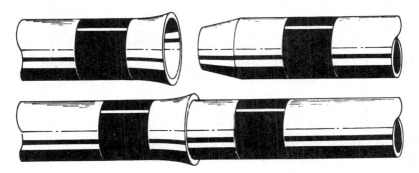

Fig. 5-10. Soil applied to pipe end for joint wiping.

Setting the pipes or fixing them rigidly in position so that they will not move during the wiping operation often taxes the ingenuity of the workman. It is an easy job on the bench, but in a building, between beams, or in other cramped places, it is often very difficult to get proper support and leave room for manipulating the solder. In bench work, the pipe may be set either with blocks and string, or with clamps.

In setting (Fig. 5-11), the pipes are supported on four blocks. At intermediate points on both sides of the pipes, nails are driven. A string is attached to the end nail and a turn taken around the opposite nail drawing the string taut; it is carried to the next nail, and the operation repeated for each pair of nails.

LENGTH OF JOINT

For guidance, Table 5-2 gives the length of joints for various-size pipes. The lengths specified in Table 5-2 represent the average

91

Table 5-2. Lengths of Wiped Joints

Pipe diameter (inches)	One-hand system		Two-hand system	
	Length of joint (inches)	Size of cloth (inches)	Length of joint (inches)	Size of cloth (inches)
$\frac{1}{2}$	2	3 × 3	$2\frac{1}{4}$	3 × 4
$\frac{3}{4}$	2	3 × 3	$2\frac{3}{8}$	3 × 4
1	2	3 × 3	$2\frac{3}{8}$	3 × 4
$1\frac{1}{4}$ water	2	3 × 3	$2\frac{1}{2}$	$3\frac{1}{4}$ × 4
$1\frac{1}{4}$ waste	2	3 × 3	$2\frac{3}{8}$	3 × 4
$1\frac{1}{2}$ water	2	3 × 3	$2\frac{1}{2}$	$3\frac{1}{4}$ × 4
$1\frac{1}{2}$ waste	2	3 × 3	$2\frac{3}{8}$	3 × 4
2 waste	2	3 × 3	$2\frac{3}{8}$	$3\frac{1}{4}$ × 4
3 waste	2	3 × 3	$2\frac{1}{2}$	$3\frac{1}{4}$ × 4
.4 waste	$1\frac{3}{4}$	3 × 3, 6 × 6	$2\frac{3}{4}$	$3\frac{1}{4}$ × 4, $3\frac{1}{4}$ × 5
2 vertical	$1\frac{3}{4}$	3 × 3	2	3 × $2\frac{1}{2}$
3 vertical	$1\frac{3}{4}$	3 × 3	2	3 × $2\frac{1}{2}$
4 vertical	$1\frac{3}{4}$	3 × 3	2	3 × $2\frac{1}{2}$

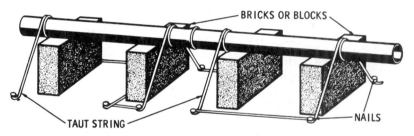

Fig. 5-11. Supporting lead pipe in preparing joint for wiping.

American practice and will be found amply large for strength and durability, and the proportions give a pleasing appearance. The table also gives the size of wiping cloths.

WIPING THE JOINT

After the pipe ends have been prepared, as just described, they are ready for the final operation of wiping. The tools needed are the furnace pot (Fig. 5-12) and ladle (Fig. 5-13) for melting and dipping out the solder, and a wiping cloth. The following information in Table 5-3 gives the amount of solder required for wiping joints of various sizes of pipe.

For joints up to 2 in. in diameter, a pot containing 10 lbs. of solder will ordinarily be large enough.

Fig. 5-12. A typical melting pot.

Fig. 5-13. A ladle for pouring solder.

There are three methods of wiping:

1. One-hand.
2. Two-hand.
3. Rolling method.

On making a joint by the one-hand method, a quantity of solder is taken from the pot by means of the ladle, the solder being previously heated so hot that the hand cannot be held closer than two inches from the surface. The solder is poured lightly on the

Table 5-3. Solder Required for Wiped Joints

Size of Pipe (inches) ...	½	¾	1	1¼	1¼ water	1½ waste
Ounces of Solder	9	12	16	16	18	18

Size of Pipe (inches) ...	1½ water	2 waste	3 waste	4 waste	4 vertical
Ounces of Solder	20	20	24	34	28

joint, the ladle being moved backward and forward, so that too much solder is not put in one place. The solder is also poured an inch or two on the soiling, to make the pipe the proper temperature. Naturally, the further the heat is run or taken along the pipe, the better the chance of making the joint. The operator keeps pouring, and with his left hand holds the cloth to catch the solder and to tin the lower side of the pipe, and also to keep the solder from dripping down. By the process of steady pouring, the solder now becomes soft and begins to feel shaped, firm, and bulky.

When in this shape and in a semifluid condition, the ladle is put down and, with the left hand, the operation of wiping (Fig. 5-14) is begun, working from the soiling toward the top of the bulb. If the solder cools rapidly, it is reheated to a plastic condition by a torch or a heated iron. When the joint is completed, it is cooled with a water spray so that the solder does not have time to alter its shape. The cloth used for wiping is a pad of moleskin or fustian about 4 in. square made from a piece of 9 × 12-in. material, folded six times and sewed to keep it from opening. The side next to the pipe is saturated with hot tallow when used. If the lead has been brought to the heat of the solder, and the latter properly manipulated and

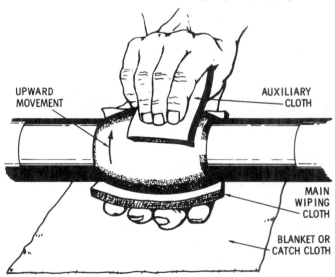

Fig. 5-14. Wiping a horizontal joint, two-hand method.

shaped while in a semifluid or plastic condition, the joint gradually assumes the finished egg-shaped appearance.

In wiping by the two-hand method, as soon as there is a sufficient body of solder around the pipe to retain the heat long enough for the wiping operation, drop the ladle and pick up a small cloth known as the auxiliary cloth. This is held in the right hand and the wiping cloth in the left hand. The metal is brought to the top of the joint by a movement of both hands, as shown in Fig. 5-14. Hold the main cloth under the joint, and with the auxiliary cloth, wipe off the surplus solder from each end and roughly mold what is left on top to the shape of the joint, throwing all the hot solder into the wiping cloth. Stock this surplus solder to the bottom of the joint and roughly mold it to the proper shape. Drop the auxiliary cloth, and finish the joint to shape with the main cloth, using both hands.

In wiping a vertical joint, a small piece of cardboard is placed under the joint to catch excess solder, as shown in Fig. 5-15, forming a flange held in place around the pipe by twine.

Fig. 5-15. Wiping a vertical joint.

WIPING A BRANCH JOINT

Usually more skill is required in preparing and wiping a branch joint than a regular joint. The operations of preparing the joint for wiping are:

95

1. Boring.
2. Expanding.
3. Flaring out.
4. Removing burrs.
5. Soiling.
6. Shaving.
7. Setting.

First, the pipe from which a branch is to run is tapped with a tap borer, as in Fig. 5-16. In using a tap borer, do not insert it far enough for its point to come into contact with the opposite side of the pipe. For ½- to 1-in. pipe, bore a ⅝-in. hole. The operations that follow consist of flaring out (Fig. 5-17), removing burrs, soiling, marking off, shaving, and setting, which are performed in a way similar to those for plain or running joints.

In setting, the parts should be secured firmly in position with clamps, blocks, etc. It will be found easier to wipe the joint by setting up the branch in the vertical position. In wiping, pour on the far and near sides, as shown in Fig. 5-18, holding the cloth at an

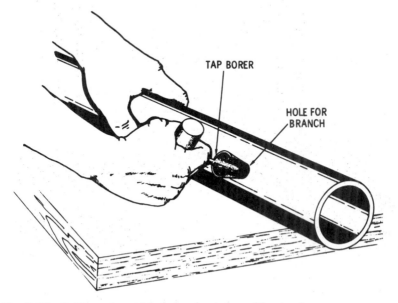

Fig. 5-16. Cutting a branch hole in a lead pipe with a tap borer.

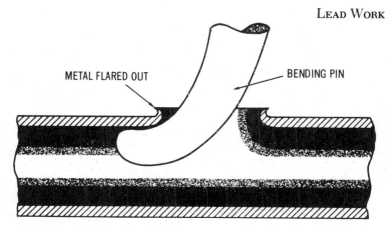

METAL FLARED OUT

BENDING PIN

Fig. 5-17. Flaring a branch hole in lead pipe.

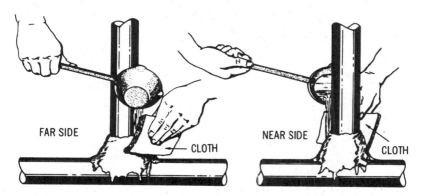

FAR SIDE

NEAR SIDE

CLOTH

CLOTH

Fig. 5-18. Pouring and wiping vertical branches.

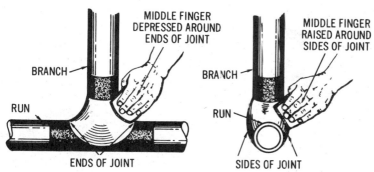

MIDDLE FINGER DEPRESSED AROUND ENDS OF JOINT

MIDDLE FINGER RAISED AROUND SIDES OF JOINT

BRANCH

BRANCH

RUN

RUN

ENDS OF JOINT

SIDES OF JOINT

Fig. 5-19. Movements in wiping vertical branches.

97

angle that will distribute the solder over the area to be covered. As the solder begins to flow, it is kept working up by manipulating the cloth. When sufficient solder has been poured to form the joint, the plumber first puts it roughly into shape with the cloth, followed by the wiping movements. The first wiping stroke encircles the branch, the solder being shaped by depressing the middle finger as the cloth is being brought around the ends of the joint, gradually raising this finger as it comes on the sides parallel to the run. These operations are shown in Fig. 5-19. The stroke should begin on the near side, as far around as possible, so the operator can entirely encircle the branch with one stroke.

CHAPTER 6

Mathematics

Plumbing and heating are important factors in construction, and are vital to the health, morale, and welfare of building occupants. Piping is the basic material in plumbing, and can be compared to the veins and arteries of the human body. Plumbing pipe is classified as supply and waste, with the supply piping providing pure water to fixtures and waste piping removing that liquid.

Design is important in planning piping systems. Piping must be durable, have leakproof joints, be of proper size for the intended purpose, and be in accordance with codes set up in almost all localities for purposes of protecting the health and welfare of the individual and public. In order to plan and compute well, a knowledge of mathematics is of great importance to the plumber and steam fitter. Therefore, a general knowledge of mathematics and access to certain reference tables is essential.

SYMBOLS

The various processes in mathematics are usually indicated by symbols for convenience and brevity. The following are symbols commonly used.

$=$ means equal to, or equality;

$-$ means minus, less, or subtraction;

$+$ means plus, or addition;

$\times$ means multiplied by, or multiplication;

$\div$ or $/$ means divided by, or division;

^{2} are indexes or powers, meaning that the number
^{3} to which they are added is to be squared or cubed;
thus, 2^2 means 2 squared; 2^3 means 2 cubed;

$:$ is to
$::$ so is $\Big\}$ are signs of proportion;
$:$ to

$\sqrt{}$ is the radical sign and means that the square root of the number before which it is placed is to be extracted;

$\sqrt[3]{}$ means that the cube root of the number before which it is placed is to be extracted;

—— the bar indicates that all of the numbers under it are to be taken together;

( ) the parentheses means that all of the numbers between are to be taken as one quantity;

the decimal point means decimal parts; thus 2.5 means 2-5/10, 0.46 means 46/100;

$^\circ$ means degrees;

$: : :$ means hence;

π means ratio of the circumference of a circle to its diameter; numerically 3.1416;

$''$ means inches, seconds, or second;

$'$ means feet, minutes, or prime.

ABBREVIATIONS

In addition to the symbols just given, certain abbreviations and definitions are used. The practice of writing "pounds per square inch" instead of "lbs. per sq. in." in not preferred because in reading it the eye has to travel faster, resulting in fatigue and less speed in reading. The same thing is true of the excessive use of capital letters. It is a psychological fact that the omission of these capital letters results in less fatigue to the reader, though he may not be conscious of the fact.

The following abbreviations are commonly used:

A or a = area
A.W.G. = American wire gauge
bbl. = barrels
B or b = breadth
bhp = brake horse power
B.M. = board measure
Btu = British thermal units
B.W.G. = Birmingham wire gauge
B & S = Brown and Sharpe wire gauge (American wire gauge)
C of g = center of gravity
cond. = condensing
cu. = cubic
cyl. = cylinder
D or d = depth or diameter
deg. = degrees
diam. = diameter
evap. = evaporation
F = coefficient of friction; Fahrenheit
F or f = force or factor of safety
ft. lbs. = foot pounds
gals. = gallons
H or h = height, or head of water
HP = horsepower
IHP = indicated horsepower
L or l = length
lbs. = pounds
lbs per sq. in. = pounds per square inch
o.d. = outside diameter (pipes)
oz. = ounces
pt. = pint
P or p = pressure or load

psi = pounds per square inch
R or r = radius
rpm = revolutions per minute
☐′ = square feet
sq. ft. = square foot
sq. in. = square inch
☐″ = square inches
sq. yd. = square yard
T or t = thickness, or temperature
temp. = temperature
V or v = velocity
vol. = volume
W or w = weight
W.I. = wrought iron

DEFINITIONS

Abstract Number—One that does not refer to any particular object.

Acute Triangle—One that has three acute angles.

Altitude (of a parallelogram or trapezoid)—the perpendicular distance between its parallel sides.

Altitude (of a prism)—The perpendicular distance between its bases.

Altitude (of a pyramid or cone)—The perpendicular distance from its vertex to the plane of its base.

Altitude (of a triangle)—A line drawn perpendicular to the base from the angle opposite.

Analysis—The process of investigating principles and solving problems independently of set rules.

Angle—The difference in direction of two lines proceeding from the same point called the vertex.

Area—The surface included within the lines that bound a plane figure.

Arithmetic—The science of numbers and the art of computation.

Base (of a triangle)—The side on which it may be supposed to stand.

Board Measure—A unit for measuring lumber being a volume of a board 12 in. wide, 1 ft. long, and 1 in. thick.

Circle—A plane figure bounded by a curved line, called the circumference, every point of which is equally distant from a point within, called the center.

Complex Fraction—One whose numerator or denominator is a fraction.

Composite Numbers—A number that can be divided by other integers besides itself and one.

Compound Fraction—A fraction of a fraction.

Compound Numbers—Units of two or more denominations of the same kind.

Concrete Numbers—A number used to designate objects of quantities.

Cone—A body having a circular base, and whose convex surface tapers uniformly to the vertex

Cube—A parallelopipedon whose faces are equal squares.

Cubic Measure—A measure of volume involving three dimensions—length, breadth, and thickness.

103

Cylinder—A body bounded by a uniformly curved surface, its ends being equal and parallel circles.

Decimal Scale—One in which the order of progression is uniformly ten.

Demonstration—Process of reasoning by which a truth or principle is established.

Denomination—Name of the unit of a concrete number.

Diagonal (of a plane figure)—A straight line joining the vertices of two angles not adjacent.

Diameter (of a circle)—A line passing through its center and terminated at both ends by the circumference.

Diameter (of a sphere)—A straight line passing through the center of the sphere, and terminated at both ends by its surface.

Equilateral Triangle—One that has all its sides equal.

Even Number—A number that can be exactly divided by two.

Exact Divisor of a Number—A whole number that will divide that number without a remainder.

Factors—One of two or more quantities that, when multiplied together, produces a given quantity.

Factors of a Number—Numbers that, when multiplied together, make that number.

Fraction—A number that expresses equal parts of a whole thing or quantity.

Frustum (of a pyramid or cone)—The part that remains after cutting off the top by a plane parallel to the base.

Geometry—The branch of pure mathematics that treats of space and its relations.

Greatest Common Divisor—The greatest number that will exactly divide two or more numbers.

Hypotenuse (of a right triangle)—The side opposite the right angle.

Improper Fraction—One whose numerator equals or exceeds its denominator.

Integer—A number that represents whole things.

Involution—The multiplication of a quantity by itself any number of times; raising a number to a given power.

Isosceles Triangle—One that has two of its sides equal.

Least Common Multiple—Least number that is exactly divisible by two or more numbers.

Like Numbers—Same kind of unit, expressing the same kind of quantity.

Mathematics—The science of quantity.

Mensuration—The process of measuring.

Measure—That by which the extent, quantity, capacity, volume, or dimensions in general is ascertained by some fixed standard.

Multiple of a Number—Any number exactly divisible by that number.

Number—A unit or collection of units.

Obtuse Triangle—One that has one obtuse angle.

Odd Number—A number that cannot be divided by two.

Parallelogram—Quadrilateral that has its opposite sides parallel.

Parallelopipedon—A prism bounded by six parallelograms, the opposite ones being parallel and equal.

Percentage—Rate per hundred.

Perimeter (of a polygon)—The sum of its sides.

Perpendicular (of a right triangle)—The side that forms a right angle with the base.

Plane Figure—A plane surface.

Polygon—A plane figure bounded by straight lines.

Power—Product arising from multiplying a number.

Prime Factor—A prime number used as a factor.

Prime Number—A number exactly divisible by some number other than one or itself.

Prism—A solid whose ends are equal and parallel polygons, and whose sides are parallelograms.

Problem—A question requiring an operation.

Proper Fraction—One whose numerator is less than its denominator.

Pyramid—A body having for its base a polygon, and for its other sides or facets three or more triangles that terminate in a common point called the vertex.

Quadrilateral—A plane figure bounded by four straight lines and having four angles.

Quantity—That which can be increased, diminished, or measured.

Radius (of a circle)—A line extending from its center to any point on the circumference. It is one-half the diameter.

Radius (of a sphere)—A straight line drawn from the center to any point on the surface.

Rectangle—A parallelogram with all its angles right angles.

Rhomboid—A parallelogram whose opposite sides only are equal, but whose angles are not right angles.

Rhombus—A parallelogram whose sides are all equal, but whose angles are not right angles.

Right Triangle—One that has a right angle.

Root—A factor repeated to produce a power.

Rule—A prescribed method of performing an operation.

Scale—Order of progression on which any system of notation is founded.

Scalene Triangle—One that has all of its sides unequal.

Simple Fraction—One whose numerator and denominator are whole numbers.

Simple Number—Either an abstract number or a concrete number of but one denomination.

Slant Height (of a cone)—A straight line from the vertex to the circumference of the base.

Slant Height (of a pyramid)—The perpendicular distance from its vertex to one of the sides of the base.

Sphere—A body bounded by a uniformly curved surface, all the points of which are equally distant from a point within called the center.

Square—A rectangle whose sides are equal.

Trapezium—A quadrilateral having no two sides parallel.

Trapezoid—A quadrilateral, two of whose sides are parallel and two oblique.

Triangle—A plane figure bounded by three sides, and having three angles.

Uniform Scale—One in which the order of progression is the same throughout the entire succession of units.

Unit—A single thing or a definite quantity.

Unity—Unit of an abstract number.

Unlike Numbers—Different kinds of units, used to express different kinds of quantity.

Varying Scale—One in which the order of progression is not the same throughout the entire succession of units.

NOTATION AND NUMERATION

By definition, *notation* in arithmetic is *the writing down of figures to express a number*. A *numeration* is *the reading of the number or collection of figures already written*.

By means of the ten figures that follow, any number can be expressed.

0 1 2 3 4 5 6 7 8 9

The system in Table 6-1A, is called *Arabic notation;* and it is the system in ordinary everyday use.

Table 6-1A. Numeration Table

Names of Units	Billions			Millions			Thousands			Units			Thousandths			
Grouping of the Units	Hundred-billions	Ten-billions	Billions	Hundred-millions	Ten-millions	Millions	Hundred-thousands	Ten-thousands	Thousands	Hundreds	Tens	Units	Decimal point	Tenths	Hundredths	Thousandths
	7	8	6,	5	4	3,	2	0	1.	2	8	2,	.	4	8	9

Table 6-1B shows the *Roman* system of notation often used, especially to denote the year of construction or manufacture.

The following ten formulas include the elementary operations of arithmetic.

1. The sum = all the parts added.
2. The difference = the minuend − the subtrahend.
3. The minuend = the subtrahend + the difference.
4. The subtrahend = the minuend − the difference.
5. The product = the multiplicand × the multiplier.
6. The multiplicand = the product ÷ the multiplier.
7. The multiplier = the product ÷ the multiplicand.
8. The quotient = the dividend ÷ the divisor.
9. The dividend = the quotient × the divisor.
10. The divisor = the dividend ÷ the quotient.

Table 6-1B. Roman Numerals

I = 1	VIII = 8	XV = 15	XL = 40	D = 500
II = 2	IX = 9	XVI = 16	L = 50	M = 1000
III = 3	X = 10	XVII = 17	LX = 60	$\overline{X}$ = 10,000
IV = 4	XI = 11	XVIII = 18	LXX = 70	$\overline{M}$ = 1,000,000
V = 5	XII = 12	XIX = 19	LXXX = 80	
VI = 6	XIII = 13	XX = 20	XC = 90	
VII = 7	XIV = 14	XXX = 30	C = 100	

Addition

The sign of addition is + and is read *plus:* thus 7 + 3 is read *seven plus three.*

Rule A—Write the numbers to be added so that like orders of units stand in the same column.

Rule B—Beginning with the lowest order, or at the right hand, add each column separately, and if the sum can be expressed by one figure, write it under the column added.

Rule C—If the sum of any column contains more than one figure, write the unit figure under the column added, and add the remaining figure or figures to the next column.

Examples:

7,060	248,124	13,579,802
9,420	4,321	93
1,743	889,966	478,652
4,004	457,902	87,547,289
22,227 Ans.		

Use great care in placing the numbers in vertical lines, as irregularity in writing them down is one cause of mistakes.

Subtraction

The sign of subtraction is $-$ and is read *minus;* thus $10 - 7$ is read *ten minus seven* or *seven from ten.*

Rule A—Write down the sum so that the units stand under the units, the tens under the tens, etc.

Rule B—Begin with the units, and take the under from the upper figure and put the remainder beneath the line.

Rule C—If the lower figure is the larger, add ten to the upper figure, and then subtract and put the remainder down; this borrowed ten must be deducted from the next column of figures where it is represented by 1.

Examples:

892	2,572	9,999
46	1,586	8,971
846 remainder		

Multiplication

The sign of multiplication is $\times$ and is read *times* or *multiplied by;* thus 6×8 is read 6 times 8, or 6 multiplied by 8. The principle of multiplication is the same as addition; thus 3 × 8 = 24 is the same as 8 + 8 + 8 = 24.

Rule—Place the unit figure of the multiplier under the unit figure of the multiplicand and proceed as in the following examples:

Example—Multiply 846 by 8; and 478,692 by 143. Arrange them thus:

```
  846              487,692
    8                  143
 6768              1463076
                   1950768
                    487692
                  69739956
```

Rule—If the multiplier has ciphers at its end, place it as in the following examples:

Example—Multiply 83567 by 50; and 898 by 2800.

```
  83567             898
     50            2800
4178350          718400
                   1796
                 2514400
```

Division

The sign of division is ÷ and is read *divided by*, thus 8 ÷ 2 is read *eight divided by two*. There are two methods of division known as *short division* and *long division*.

Short Division
To divide by any number up to 12.
Rule—Put the dividend down with the divisor to the left of it, with a small curved line separating it, as in the following:

Example—Divide 7,865,432 by 6.

```
6)7,865,432
  1,310,905 —2
```

111

Here at the last, 6 into 32 goes 5 times and 2 over; always place the number that is left over as a fraction. This would be $\frac{2}{6}$, the top figure being the remainder and the bottom figure the divisor. It should be put close to the quotient; thus 1,310,905 $\frac{2}{6}$.

To divide by any number up to 12 with a cipher or ciphers after it, as 20, 70, 500, 7000, etc.

Rule—Place the sum down as in the last example, then mark off from the right of the dividend as many figures as there are ciphers in the divisor; also mark off the ciphers in the divisor; then divide the remaining figures by the number remaining in the divisor, thus:

Example—Divide 9,876,804 by 40.

$$\frac{40)9,876,804}{246,920 \ \ 4/40}$$

Long Division

To divide any number by a large divisor of two or more figures.

Example—Divide 18,149 by 56.

$$
\begin{array}{r}
56) \ 18149(324 \ 5/56 \\
\underline{168} \\
134 \\
\underline{112} \\
229 \\
\underline{224} \\
5
\end{array}
$$

In the above operation, the process is as follows: As neither 1 nor 18 will contain the divisor, take the first three figures (181) for the first partial dividend. The number 56 is contained in 181 three times, with a remainder. Write the 3 as the first figure in the quotient, and then multiply the divisor by this quotient figure thus: 3 times 56 is 168, which when subtracted from 181 leaves 13. To this remainder annex bring down 4, the next figure in the dividend, thus forming 134 which is the next partial dividend. The number

56 is contained in 134 two times with a remainder. Thus, 2 times 56 is 112, which subtracted from 134 leaves 22. To the remainder bring down 9, the last figure in the dividend, forming 229, the last partial dividend. The number 56 is contained in 229 four times with a remainder. Thus: 4 times 56 is 224, which, subtracted from 229 gives 5, the final remainder; thus completing the operation of long division.

Factors

Numbers 4 and 5 are factors of 20, because 4 multiplied by 5 equals 20.

Rule—Divide the given number by any prime factor; divide the quotient in the same manner, and so continue the division until the quotient is a prime number. The several divisors and the last quotient will be the prime factors required.

Example—What are the prime factors of 798?

$$
\begin{array}{r|r}
2 & 798 \\
3 & 399 \\
7 & 133 \\
19 & 19 \\
\end{array}
$$

Greatest Common Divisor

Number 5 is the greatest common divisor of 10 and 15, because it is the greatest number that will exactly divide each of them.

Rule—Write the numbers in a line, with a vertical line at the left, and divide by any factor common to all the numbers. Divide the quotient in like manner, and continue dividing till a set of quotients is obtained that are prime to each other. Multiply all the divisors together and the product will be the greatest common divisor sought.

Example—What is the greatest common divisor of 72, 120, and 440?

$$
\begin{array}{r|rrr}
4 & 72 & 120 & 440 \\
2 & 18 & 30 & 110 \\
& 9 & 15 & 55 \\
\end{array}
$$

Least Common Divisor

Number 6 is the least common multiple of 2 and 3, because it is the least number exactly divisible by those numbers.

Rule—Resolve the given numbers into their prime factors. Multiply together all the prime factors of the largest number, and such prime factors of the other numbers as are not found in the largest number. Their product will be the least common multiple. When a prime factor is repeated in any of the given numbers it must be taken as many times in the multiple as the greatest number of times it appears in any of the given numbers.

Example—Find the least common multiple of 60, 84, and 132.

$$60 = 2 \times 2 \times 3 \times 5$$
$$84 = 2 \times 2 \times 3 \times 7$$
$$132 = 2 \times 2 \times 2 \times 3 \times 11$$
$$(2 \times 2 \times 3 \times 11) \times 5 \times 7 = 4620$$

Fractions

If a unit or whole number is divided into two equal parts, one of these parts is called *one-half*, written $\frac{1}{2}$.

To reduce a common fraction to its lowest terms:
Rule—Divide both terms by their greatest common divisor.

Example:

$$\frac{9}{15} = \frac{3}{5}$$

To change an improper fraction to a mixed number:
Rule—Divide the numerator by the denominator; the quotient is the whole number, and the remainder placed over the denominator is the fraction.

Example:

$$\frac{23}{4} = 5\frac{3}{4}$$

To change a mixed number to an improper fraction:

Rule—Multiply the whole number by the denominator of the fraction; to the product add the numerator and place the sum over the denominator.

Example:

$$1\tfrac{3}{8} = \frac{11}{8}$$

To reduce a compound to a single fraction, and to multiply fractions:

Rule—Multiply the numerators together for a new numerator and the denominators together for a new denominator.

Example:

$$\frac{1}{2} \text{ of } \frac{2}{3} = \frac{2}{6}; \text{ also } \frac{1}{2} \times \frac{2}{3} = \frac{2}{6}$$

To reduce a complex to a simple fraction:

Rule—The numerator and denominator must each first be given the form of a simple fraction: then multiply the numerator of the upper fraction by the denominator of the lower for the new numerator, and the denominator of the upper by the numerator of the lower for the new denominator.

Example:

$$\frac{7/8}{1\text{-}3/4} = \frac{7/8}{7/4} = \frac{28}{56} = \frac{1}{2}$$

To add fractions:

Rule—Reduce them to a common denominator, add the numerators, and place their sum over the common denominator.

Example:

$$\frac{1}{2} + \frac{1}{4} = \frac{4+2}{8} = \frac{6}{8} = \frac{3}{4}$$

To subtract fractions:

Rule—Reduce them to a common denominator, subtract the

115

numerators, and place the difference over the common denominator.

Example:

$$\frac{1}{2} - \frac{1}{4} = \frac{4 - 2}{8} = \frac{2}{8} = \frac{1}{4}$$

To multiply fractions:

Rule—(Multiplying by a whole number) Multiply the numerator or divide the denominator by the whole number.

Example:

$$\frac{1}{2} \times 3 = \frac{3}{2} = 1\frac{1}{2}$$

To divide fractions:

Rule—(Dividing by a whole number) Divide the numerator, or multiply the denominator by the whole number.

Example:

(dividing) $\frac{10}{13} \div 5 = \frac{2}{13}$; (multiplying) $\frac{10}{13} \div 5 = \frac{10}{65} = \frac{2}{13}$

Rule—(Dividing by a fraction) Invert the divisor and proceed as in multiplication.

Example:

$$\frac{3}{4} \div \frac{5}{7} = \frac{3}{4} \times \frac{7}{5} = \frac{21}{20} = 1\frac{1}{20}$$

DECIMAL FRACTIONS

Any decimal or combination of a decimal and integer may be read by applying Table 6-2.

The important thing about decimals is to always plainly put down the decimal point. In case of a column of figures, as in

Table 6-2. Numeration of Decimals

Ten thousands	Thousands	Hundreds	Tens	Units	Decimal point	Tenths	Hundredths	Thousandths	Ten thousandths	Hundred thousandths
1	2	3	4	5	.	1	2	3	4	5
5th order	4th order	3rd order	2nd order	1st order		1st order	2nd order	3rd order	4th order	5th order

Integers	Decimals

addition, care should be taken to have all the decimal points exactly under each other.

To reduce a decimal to a common fraction:

Rule—Write down the denominator and reduce the common fraction thus obtained to its lowest terms.

Example:

$$.25 = \frac{25}{100} = \frac{1}{4}$$

To add and subtract decimals:

Rule—Place the numbers in a column with the decimal points under each other and proceed as in simple addition or subtraction.

Examples:

Addition   Subtraction

.5   1.25
.25   .75
1.75   .50
2.50

To multiply decimals:

Rule—Proceed as in simple multiplication and point off as many places as there are places in the multiplier and multiplicand.

Example:

$$.1 \times .0025 = .00025$$

To divide decimals:

Rule—Proceed as in simple division, and from the right hand of the quotient, point off as many places for decimals as the decimal places in the dividend exceed those in the divisor.

Example:

$$1.5 \div .25 = 6$$

To reduce common fractions to decimals:

Rule—Divide the numerator by the denominator and carry out the division to as many decimal places as desired.

Example:

$$\frac{4}{5} = 4 \div 5 = .8$$

The decimal equivalents of common fractions given in Table 6-3 will be found very useful.

RATIO AND PROPORTION

A ratio is virtually a fraction. When two ratios are equal, the four terms form a proportion. Thus 2:4: :3:6, which is read as, 2 is to 4

Table 6-3. Fractions and Decimal Equivalents

$\frac{1}{64} = .015625$	$\frac{11}{32} = .34375$	$\frac{43}{64} = .671875$
$\frac{1}{32} = .03125$	$\frac{23}{64} = .359375$	$\frac{11}{16} = .6875$
$\frac{3}{64} = .046875$	$\frac{3}{8} = .375$	$\frac{45}{64} = .703125$
$\frac{1}{16} = .0625$	$\frac{25}{64} = .390625$	$\frac{23}{32} = .71875$
$\frac{5}{64} = .078125$	$\frac{13}{32} = .40625$	$\frac{47}{64} = .734375$
$\frac{3}{32} = .09375$	$\frac{27}{64} = .421875$	$\frac{3}{4} = .75$
$\frac{7}{64} = .109375$	$\frac{7}{16} = .4375$	$\frac{49}{64} = .765625$
$\frac{1}{8} = .125$	$\frac{29}{64} = .453125$	$\frac{25}{32} = .78125$
$\frac{9}{64} = .140625$	$\frac{15}{32} = .46875$	$\frac{51}{64} = .796875$
$\frac{5}{32} = .15625$	$\frac{31}{64} = .484375$	$\frac{13}{16} = .8125$
$\frac{11}{64} = .171875$	$\frac{1}{2} = .5$	$\frac{53}{64} = .828125$
$\frac{3}{16} = .1875$	$\frac{33}{64} = .515625$	$\frac{27}{32} = .84375$
$\frac{13}{64} = .203125$	$\frac{17}{32} = .53125$	$\frac{55}{64} = .859375$
$\frac{7}{32} = .21875$	$\frac{35}{64} = .546875$	$\frac{7}{8} = .875$
$\frac{15}{16} = .234375$	$\frac{9}{16} = .5625$	$\frac{57}{64} = .890625$
$\frac{1}{4} = .25$	$\frac{37}{64} = .578125$	$\frac{29}{32} = .90625$
$\frac{17}{64} = .265625$	$\frac{19}{32} = .59375$	$\frac{59}{64} = .921875$
$\frac{9}{32} = .28125$	$\frac{39}{64} = .609375$	$\frac{15}{16} = .9375$
$\frac{19}{64} = .296875$	$\frac{5}{8} = .625$	$\frac{61}{64} = .953125$
$\frac{5}{16} = .3125$	$\frac{41}{64} = .640625$	$\frac{31}{32} = .96875$
$\frac{21}{64} = .328125$	$\frac{21}{32} = .65625$	$\frac{63}{64} = .984375$

as 3 is to 6. Sometimes the $=$ sign is placed between the two ratios instead of the sign : :, thus 2:4 = 3:6.

Rule—Two quantities of *different* kinds cannot form the terms of a ratio.

Rule—The product of the extremes equals the product of the means.

Example:

$$4:8 = 2:4, \text{ or } 4 \times 4 = 8 \times 2, \text{ or } 16 = 16$$

Rule of Three—When three terms of a proportion are given, the method of finding the fourth term is called the *rule of three*.

Example—If five boxes of nails cost $16, what will 25 boxes cost? Let X equal the unknown term; then

$$5 \text{ boxes} : 25 \text{ boxes} = \$16 : \$X.$$

$$5 \times X = 25 \times 16$$

$$X = \frac{25 \times 16}{5} = \$80$$

119

PERCENTAGE

A profit of 6% means a gain of $6 on every $100. Note carefully with respect to the symbol %. 5% means 5/100 which, when reduced to a decimal (as is necessary in making a calculation), becomes .05. However, .05% has a quite different value; thus, 0.05% means .05/100 which, when reduced to a decimal, becomes .0005; that is, 5/100 of 1%.

Rule—If the decimal has more than two places, the figures that follow the hundredths place signify parts of 1%.

Example—If the list price of screws is $16 per 1000, what is the net cost with 5% discount for cash?

$$5\% = \frac{5}{100} = .05;\ 16 \times .05 = 80¢;\ \$16 - 80¢ = \$15.20$$

POWERS OF NUMBERS

The *square* of a number is its second power; the *cube*, its third power. Thus,

the square of 2 = 2 × 2 = 4; the cube of 2 = 2 × 2 × 2 = 8

The power to which a number is raised is indicated by a small *superior* figure called an *exponent*. Thus,

$$2^2 = 2 \times 2 = 4;\ 2^3 = 2 \times 2 \times 2 = 8$$

ROOTS OF NUMBERS (EVOLUTION)

In the equation 2 × 2 = 4, the number 2 is the root for which the power (4) is produced. The radical sign $\sqrt{}$ placed over a number means the root of the number is to be extracted. Thus $\sqrt{4}$ means that the square root of 4 is to be extracted. The *index* of the root is a small figure placed over the radical.

Rule—(Square root). As shown in the example, point off the

given number into groups of two places each, beginning with units. If there are decimals, point these off likewise, beginning at the decimal point and supplying as many ciphers as may be needed. Find the greatest number whose square is less than the first left-hand group, and place it as the first figure in the quotient. Subtract its square from the left-hand group, and annex the two figures of the second group to the remainder for a dividend. Double the first figure of the quotient for a partial divisor; find how many times the latter is contained in the dividend, exclusive of the right-hand figure in the quotient, and annex it to the right of the partial divisor, forming the complete divisor. Multiply this divisor by the second figure in the quotient, and subtract the product from the dividend. To the remainder, bring down the next group and proceed as before, in each case doubling the figures in the root already found to obtain the trial divisor. Should the product of the second figure in the root by the completed divisor be greater than the dividend, erase the second figure both from the quotient and from the divisor, and substitute the next smaller figure, or one small enough to make the product of the second figure by the divisor less than or equal to the dividend.

Example:

$$
\begin{array}{r|l}
3.'14'15'92'65'36' & \underline{1.77245+} \\
1 & \\
\end{array}
$$

```
           3.'14'15'92'65'36' |1.77245+
           1
     27 |214
        |189
    347 |2515
        |2429
   3542 |8692
        |7084
  35444 |160865
        |141776
 354485 |1908936
        |1772425
```

Rule—(Cube root). As shown in the example, separate the number into groups of three figures each, beginning at the units. Find the greatest cube in the left-hand group and write its root

121

for the first figure of the required root. Cube this root, subtract the result from the left-hand group, and to the remainder annex the next group for a dividend. For a partial divisor, take three times the square of the root already found (considered as tens), and divide the dividend by it. The quotient (or the quotient diminished) will be the second figure of the root. To this partial divisor add three times the product of the first figure on the root (considered as tens) by the second figure, and also the square of the second figure. This sum will be the complete divisor. Multiply the complete divisor by the second figure of the root, subtract the product from the dividend, and to the remainder annex the next group for a new dividend. Proceed in this manner until all the groups have been annexed. The result will be the cube root required. Table 6-4 can be a great help in determining the square, cube, square root, or cube root of numbers up to 100.

Example:

$$1',881',365',963',625' \quad 12345$$

$$
\begin{array}{rl}
300 \times 1^2 & = 300 \quad \overline{881} \\
30 \times 1 \quad \times 2 & = \ \ 60 \\
2^2 & = \ \ \underline{\ \ 4} \\
& \ \ 364 \quad \underline{728} \\
& \qquad \quad 153365
\end{array}
$$

$$
\begin{array}{rl}
300 \times 12^2 & = 43200 \\
30 \times 12 \quad \times 3 & = \ \ 1080 \\
3^2 & = \ \ \ \ \ \underline{9} \\
& \ 44289 \quad \underline{132867} \\
& \qquad \qquad 20498963
\end{array}
$$

$$
\begin{array}{rl}
300 \times 123^2 & = 4538700 \\
30 \times 123 \quad \times 4 & = \ \ \ 14760 \\
4^2 & = \ \ \ \ \ \ \ \underline{16} \\
& 4553476 \quad \underline{18213904} \\
& \qquad \qquad \ \ \ \ 2285059625
\end{array}
$$

$$
\begin{array}{rl}
300 \times 1234^2 & = 456826800 \\
30 \times 1234 \quad \times 5 & = \ \ \ 185100 \\
5^2 & = \ \ \ \ \ \ \ \ \ \underline{25} \\
& 457011925 \quad 2285059625
\end{array}
$$

MATHEMATICS

Table 6-4. Squares, Cubes, Square Roots, and Cube Roots

No.	Square	Cube	Square Root	Cube Root	Reciprocal
1	1	1	1.00000	1.00000	1.00000
2	4	8	1.41421	1.25992	0.50000
3	9	27	1.73205	1.44224	0.33333
4	16	64	2.00000	1.58740	0.25000
5	25	125	2.23606	1.70997	0.20000
6	36	216	2.44948	1.81712	0.16666
7	49	343	2.64575	1.91293	0.14285
8	64	512	2.82842	2.00000	0.12500
9	81	729	3.00000	2.08008	0.11111
10	100	1000	3.16227	2.15443	0.10000
11	121	1331	3.31662	2.22398	0.09090
12	144	1728	3.46410	2.28942	0.08333
13	169	2197	3.60555	2.35133	0.07602
14	196	2744	3.74165	2.41014	0.07142
15	225	3375	3.87298	2.46621	0.06666
16	256	4096	4.00000	2.51984	0.06250
17	289	4913	4.12310	2.57128	0.05882
18	324	5832	4.24264	2.62074	0.05555
19	361	6859	4.35889	2.66840	0.05263
20	400	8000	4.47213	2.71441	0.05000
21	441	9621	4.58257	2.75892	0.04761
22	484	10648	4.69041	2.80203	0.04545
23	529	12167	4.79583	2.84386	0.04347
24	576	13824	4.89897	2.88449	0.04166
25	625	15625	5.00000	2.92401	0.04000
26	676	17576	5.09901	2.96249	0.03846
27	729	19683	5.19615	3.00000	0.03703
28	784	21952	5.29150	3.03658	0.03571
29	841	24389	5.38516	3.07231	0.03448
30	900	27000	5.47722	3.10723	0.03333
31	961	29791	5.56776	3.14138	0.03225
32	1024	32768	5.65685	3.17480	0.03125
33	1089	35937	5.74456	3.20753	0.03030
34	1156	39304	5.83095	3.23961	0.02941
35	1225	42875	5.91607	3.27106	0.02857
36	1296	46656	6.00000	3.30192	0.02777
37	1369	50653	6.08276	3.33222	0.02702
38	1444	54872	6.16441	3.36197	0.02631
39	1521	59319	6.24499	3.39121	0.02564
40	1600	64000	6.32455	3.41995	0.02500
41	1681	68921	6.40312	3.44821	0.02439
42	1764	74088	6.48074	3.47602	0.02380
43	1849	79507	6.55743	3.50339	0.02325
44	1936	85184	6.63324	3.53034	0.02272
45	2025	91125	6.70820	3.55689	0.02222
46	2116	97336	6.78233	3.58304	0.02173
47	2209	103823	6.85565	3.60882	0.02127
48	2304	110592	6.92820	3.63424	0.02083
49	2401	117649	7.00000	3.65930	0.02040
50	2500	125000	7.07106	3.68403	0.02000

123

Table 6-4. Squares, Cubes, Square Roots, and Cube Roots (Cont'd)

No.	Square	Cube	Square Root	Cube Root	Reciprocal
51	2601	132651	7.14142	3.70842	0.01960
52	2704	140608	7.21110	3.73251	0.01923
53	2809	148877	7.28010	3.75628	0.01886
54	2916	157464	7.34846	3.77976	0.01851
55	3025	166375	7.41619	3.80295	0.01818
56	3136	175616	7.48331	3.82586	0.01785
57	3249	185193	7.54983	3.84850	0.01754
58	3364	195112	7.61577	3.87087	0.01724
59	3481	205379	7.68114	3.89299	0.01694
60	3600	216000	7.74596	3.91486	0.01666
61	3721	226981	7.81024	3.93649	0.01639
62	3844	238328	7.87400	3.95789	0.01612
63	3969	250047	7.93725	3.97905	0.01587
64	4096	262144	8.00000	4.00000	0.01562
65	4225	274625	8.06225	4.02072	0.01538
66	4356	287496	8.12403	4.04124	0.01515
67	4489	300763	8.18535	4.06154	0.01492
68	4624	314432	8.24621	4.08165	0.01470
69	4761	328509	8.30662	4.10156	0.01449
70	4900	343000	8.36660	4.12128	0.01428
71	5041	357911	8.42614	4.14081	0.01408
72	5184	373248	8.48528	4.16016	0.01388
73	5329	389017	8.54400	4.17933	0.01369
74	5476	405224	8.60232	4.19833	0.01351
75	5625	421875	8.66025	4.21716	0.01333
76	5776	438976	8.71779	4.23582	0.01315
77	5929	456533	8.77496	4.25432	0.01298
78	6084	474552	8.83176	4.27265	0.01282
79	6241	493039	8.88819	4.29084	0.01265
80	6400	512000	8.94427	4.30886	0.01250
81	6561	531441	9.00000	4.32674	0.01234
82	6724	551368	9.05538	4.34448	0.01219
83	6889	571787	9.11043	4.36207	0.01204
84	7056	592704	9.16515	4.37951	0.01190
85	7225	614125	9.21954	4.39682	0.01176
86	7396	636056	9.27361	4.41400	0.01162
87	7569	658503	9.32737	4.43104	0.01149
88	7744	681472	9.38083	4.44796	0.01136
89	7921	704969	9.43398	4.46474	0.01123
90	8100	729000	9.48683	4.48140	0.01111
91	8281	753571	9.53939	4.49794	0.01098
92	8464	778688	9.59166	4.51435	0.01086
93	8649	804357	9.64365	4.53065	0.01075
94	8836	830584	9.69535	4.54683	0.01063
95	9025	857375	9.74679	4.56290	0.01052
96	9216	884736	9.79795	4.57885	0.01041
97	9409	912673	9.84885	4.59470	0.01030
98	9604	941192	9.89949	4.61043	0.01020
99	9801	970299	9.94987	4.62606	0.01010
100	10000	1000000	10.00000	4.64158	0.01000

Rule—(Roots higher than the cube). The fourth root is the square root of the square root; the sixth root is the cube root of the square root, or the square root of the cube root. Other roots are most conveniently found by the use of logarithms.

THE METRIC SYSTEM

The important feature of the metric system is that it is based upon the *decimal scale*. Thus, a knowledge of decimals is needed before taking up this system.

The metric system is the decimal system of measures and weights, with the meter and the gram as the bases. The unit of length (the meter) was intended to be, and is very nearly one ten-millionth part of the distance measured on a meridian from the equator to the pole, or 39.37079 inches. The other primary units of measure such as the *square meter*, the *cubic meter*, the *liter*, and the *gram* are based on the meter.

Following is the *metric* system of weights and measures. Table 6-5 shows the conversion of millimeters into inches, and Table 6-6 shows the conversion of inches into millimeters.

Milli expresses the 1000th part.
Centi expresses the 100th part.
Deci expresses the 10th part.
Deka expresses 10 times the value.
Hecto expresses 100 times the value.
Kilo expresses 1000 times the value.

Length

1 mm.	= 1 Millimeter	= 1/1000 of a meter	=	.03937 in.
10 mm.	= 1 Centimeter	= 1/100 of a meter	=	.3937 in.
10 cm.	= 1 Decimeter	= 1/10 of a meter	=	3.937 in.
10 dm.	= 1 Meter	= 1 meter	=	39.37 in.
10 m.	= 1 Dekameter	= 10 meters	=	32.8 ft.
10 Dm.	= 1 Hectometer	= 100 meters	=	328.09 ft.
10 Hm.	= 1 Kilometer	= 1000 meters	=	.62137 mile.

125

Table 6-5. Millimeters to Inches

mm.	inches		mm.	inches		mm.	inches
$^1/_{50}$ = 0.00079			$^{26}/_{50}$ = 0.02047			2 = 0.07874	
$^2/_{50}$ = 0.00157			$^{27}/_{50}$ = 0.02126			3 = 0.11811	
$^3/_{50}$ = 0.00236			$^{28}/_{50}$ = 0.02205			4 = 0.15748	
$^4/_{50}$ = 0.00315			$^{29}/_{50}$ = 0.02283			5 = 0.19685	
$^5/_{50}$ = 0.00394			$^{30}/_{50}$ = 0.02362			6 = 0.23622	
$^6/_{50}$ = 0.00472			$^{31}/_{50}$ = 0.02441			7 = 0.27559	
$^7/_{50}$ = 0.00551			$^{32}/_{50}$ = 0.02520			8 = 0.31496	
$^8/_{50}$ = 0.00630			$^{33}/_{50}$ = 0.02598			9 = 0.35433	
$^9/_{50}$ = 0.00709			$^{34}/_{50}$ = 0.02677			10 = 0.39370	
$^{10}/_{50}$ = 0.00787			$^{35}/_{50}$ = 0.02756			11 = 0.43307	
$^{11}/_{50}$ = 0.00866			$^{36}/_{50}$ = 0.02835			12 = 0.47244	
$^{12}/_{50}$ = 0.00945			$^{37}/_{50}$ = 0.02913			13 = 0.51181	
$^{13}/_{50}$ = 0.01024			$^{38}/_{50}$ = 0.02992			14 = 0.55118	
$^{14}/_{50}$ = 0.01102			$^{39}/_{50}$ = 0.03071			15 = 0.59055	
$^{15}/_{50}$ = 0.01181			$^{40}/_{50}$ = 0.03150			16 = 0.62992	
$^{16}/_{50}$ = 0.01260			$^{41}/_{50}$ = 0.03228			17 = 0.66929	
$^{17}/_{50}$ = 0.01339			$^{42}/_{50}$ = 0.03307			18 = 0.70866	
$^{18}/_{50}$ = 0.01417			$^{43}/_{50}$ = 0.03386			19 = 0.74803	
$^{19}/_{50}$ = 0.01496			$^{44}/_{50}$ = 0.03465			20 = 0.78740	
$^{20}/_{50}$ = 0.01575			$^{45}/_{50}$ = 0.03543			21 = 0.82677	
$^{21}/_{50}$ = 0.01654			$^{46}/_{50}$ = 0.03622			22 = 0.86614	
$^{22}/_{50}$ = 0.01732			$^{47}/_{50}$ = 0.03701			23 = 0.90551	
$^{23}/_{50}$ = 0.01811			$^{48}/_{50}$ = 0.03780			24 = 0.94488	
$^{24}/_{50}$ = 0.01890			$^{49}/_{50}$ = 0.03858			25 = 0.98425	
$^{25}/_{50}$ = 0.01969			1 = 0.03937			26 = 1.02362	

Square Measure

1 sq. centimeter = 0.1550 sq. in.

1 sq. in. = 6.452 sq. centimeters

1 sq. decimeter = 0.1076 sq. ft.

1 sq. ft. = 9.2903 sq. decimeters

1 sq. meter = 1.196 sq. yd.

1 sq. yd. = 0.8361 sq. meter

1 acre = 3.954 sq. rod

1 sq. rod = 0.2529 acre

1 hectare = 2.47 acres

1 acre = 0.4047 hectare

1 sq. kilometer = 0.386 sq. mile

1 sq. mile = 2.59 sq. kilometers

Table 6-6. Inches to Millimeters

In.	0	$\frac{1}{16}$	$\frac{1}{8}$	$\frac{3}{16}$	$\frac{7}{16}$	$\frac{1}{4}$	$\frac{5}{16}$	$\frac{3}{8}$
0	0.0	1.6	3.2	4.8	6.4	7.9	9.5	11.1
1	25.4	27.0	28.6	30.2	31.7	33.3	34.9	36.5
2	50.8	52.4	54.0	55.6	57.1	58.7	60.3	61.9
3	76.2	77.8	79.4	81.0	82.5	84.1	85.7	87.3
4	101.6	103.2	104.8	106.4	108.0	109.5	111.1	112.7
5	127.0	128.6	130.2	131.8	133.4	134.9	136.5	138.1
6	152.4	154.0	155.6	157.2	158.8	160.3	161.9	163.5
7	177.8	179.4	181.0	182.6	184.2	185.7	187.3	188.9
8	203.2	204.8	206.4	208.0	209.6	211.1	212.7	214.3
9	228.6	230.2	231.8	233.4	235.0	236.5	238.1	239.7
10	254.0	255.6	257.2	258.8	260.4	261.9	263.5	265.1
11	279.4	281.0	282.6	284.2	285.7	287.3	288.9	290.5
12	304.8	306.4	308.0	309.6	311.1	312.7	314.3	315.9
13	330.2	331.8	333.4	335.0	336.5	338.1	339.7	341.3
14	355.6	357.2	358.8	360.4	361.9	363.5	365.1	366.7
15	381.0	382.6	384.2	385.8	387.3	388.9	390.5	392.1
16	406.4	408.0	409.6	411.2	412.7	414.3	415.9	417.5
17	431.8	433.4	435.0	436.6	438 1	439.7	441.3	442.9
18	457.2	458.8	460.4	462.0	463.5	465.1	466.7	468.3
19	482.6	484.2	485.8	487.4	488.9	490.5	492.1	493.7
20	508.0	509.6	511.2	512 8	514.3	515.9	517.5	519.1
21	533.4	535.0	536.6	538.2	539.7	541.3	542.9	544.5
22	558.8	560.4	562.0	563.6	565.1	566.7	568.3	569.9
23	584.2	585.8	587.4	589.0	590.5	592.1	593.7	595.3

In.	$\frac{1}{2}$	$\frac{9}{16}$	$\frac{5}{8}$	$\frac{11}{16}$	$\frac{3}{4}$	$\frac{13}{16}$	$\frac{7}{8}$	$\frac{15}{16}$
0	12.7	14.3	15.9	17.5	19.1	20.6	22.2	23.8
1	38.1	39.7	41.3	42.9	44.4	46 0	47.6	49.2
2	63.5	65.1	66.7	68.3	69.8	71.4	73.0	74.6
3	88.9	90.5	92.1	93.7	95.2	96.8	98.4	100.0
4	114.3	115.9	117.5	119.1	120.7	122.2	123.8	125.4
5	139.7	141.3	142.9	144.5	146.1	147.6	149.2	150.8
6	165.1	166.7	168.3	169.9	171.5	173.0	174.6	176.2
7	190.5	192.1	193.7	195.3	196.9	198.4	200.0	201.6
8	215.9	217.5	219.1	220.7	222.3	223.8	225.4	227.0
9	241.3	242.9	244.5	246.1	247.7	249.2	250.8	252.4
10	266.7	268.3	269.9	271.5	273.1	274.6	276.2	277.8
11	292.1	293.7	295.3	296.9	298.4	300.0	301.6	303.2
12	317.5	319.1	320.7	322.3	323.8	325.4	327.0	328.6
13	342.9	344.5	346.1	347.7	349.2	350.8	352.4	354.0
14	368.3	369.9	371.5	373.1	374.6	376 2	377.8	379.4
15	393.7	395.3	396.9	398.5	400.0	401.6	403.2	404.8
16	419.1	420.7	422.3	423.9	425.4	427.0	428.6	430.2
17	444.5	446.1	447.7	449.3	450.8	452.4	454.0	455.6
18	469.9	471.5	473.1	474.7	476.2	477.3	479.4	481.0
19	495.3	496.9	498.5	500.1	501.6	503.2	504.8	506.4
20	520.7	522.3	523.9	525.5	527.0	528.6	530.2	531.8
21	546.1	547.7	549.3	550.9	552.4	554.0	555.6	557.2
22	571.5	573.1	574.7	576.3	577.8	579.4	581.0	582.6
23	596.9	598.5	600.1	601.7	603.2	604 8	606.4	608.0

Table Weights

1 gram = 0.0527 ounce	1 ounce = 28.35 grams
1 kilogram = 2.2046 lbs.	1 lb. = 0.4536 kilogram
1 metric ton = 1.1023 English ton	1 English ton = 0.9072 metric ton

Approximate Metric Equivalents

1 decimeter = 4 inches	1 liter = 1.06 qt. liquid; 0.9 qt. dry
1 meter = 1.1 yards	
1 kilometer = ⅝ mile	1 hectoliter = 2⅝ bushel
1 hectare = 2½ acres	1 kilogram = 2⅕ lbs.
1 stere or cu. meter = ¼ cord	1 metric ton = 2200 lbs.

Long Measure

12 inches (in. or ″)	= 1 foot (ft. or ′)
3 feet	= 1 yard (yd.)
5½ yards or 16½ feet	= 1 rod (rd.)
40 rods	= 1 furlong (fur.)
8 furlongs or 320 rods	= 1 statute mile (mi.)

Nautical Measure

6080.26 ft. or 1.15156 statute miles	= 1 nautical mile
3 nautical miles	= 1 league
60 nautical miles or 69.168 statute miles	= 1 degree (at the equator)
360 degrees	= circumference of earth at equator

Square Measure

144 square inches (sq. in.)	= 1 square foot (sq. ft.)
9 sq. ft.	= 1 square yard (sq. yd.)
30¼ sq. yd.	= 1 square rod or perch (sq. rd.) or P.)
640 acres	= 1 square mile (sq. mi.)

MENSURATION

Mensuration is the process of measuring objects that occupy space; for instance, finding the length of a line, the area of a triangle, or the volume of a cube.

Triangles

Figures bounded by three sides are called triangles; there are numerous kinds due to varying angles and length of sides.

To find the length of the hypotenuse of a right triangle:
Rule—The hypotenuse is equal to the square root of the sum of the squares of each leg, as shown in Fig. 6-1.

To find the length of either leg of a right triangle:
Rule—Either leg is equal to the square root of the difference between the square of the hypotenuse and the square of the other leg (Fig. 6-1).

To find the area of any triangle:
Rule—Multiply the base by half the perpendicular height. Thus, if the base is 12 ft. and the height 8 ft., the area = $\frac{1}{2}$ of $8 \times 12 = 48$ sq. ft.

Quadrilaterals

Any plain figure bounded by four sides is a quadrilateral, as shown in Fig. 6-2.

To find the area of a trapezium:
Rule—Join two of its opposite angles, and thus divide it into two triangles. Measure this line and call it the base of each triangle. Measure the perpendicular height of each triangle above the base line. Then find the area of each triangle by the previous rule; their sum is the area of the whole figure.

To find the area of a trapezoid:
Rule—Multiply half the sum of the two parallel sides by the perpendicular distance between them.

129

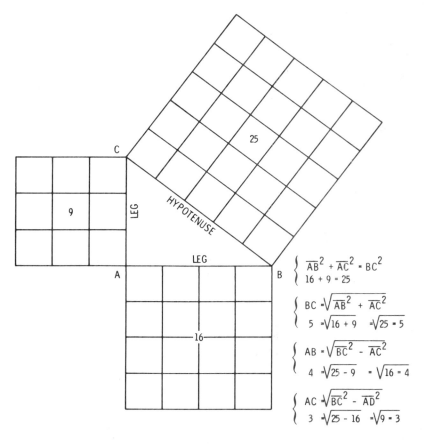

$$\begin{cases} \overline{AB}^2 + \overline{AC}^2 = BC^2 \\ 16 + 9 = 25 \end{cases}$$

$$\begin{cases} BC = \sqrt{\overline{AB}^2 + \overline{AC}^2} \\ 5 = \sqrt{16 + 9} = \sqrt{25} = 5 \end{cases}$$

$$\begin{cases} AB = \sqrt{\overline{BC}^2 - \overline{AC}^2} \\ 4 = \sqrt{25 - 9} = \sqrt{16} = 4 \end{cases}$$

$$\begin{cases} AC = \sqrt{\overline{BC}^2 - \overline{AD}^2} \\ 3 = \sqrt{25 - 16} = \sqrt{9} = 3 \end{cases}$$

Fig. 6-1. Right triangle showing mathematical relationships.

To find the area of a square:
Rule—Multiply the base by the height; that is, multiply the length by the breadth.

To find the area of a rectangle:
Rule—Multiply the length by the breadth.

To find the area of a parallelogram:
Rule—Multiply the base by the perpendicular height.

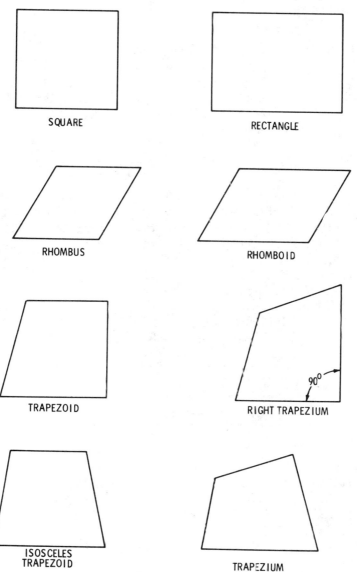

Fig. 6-2. Various quadrilaterals.

Polygons

These comprise the numerous figures having more than four sides, named according to the number of sides, thus:

pentagon ....5 sides
hexagon ....6 sides
heptagon ....7 sides
octagon ....8 sides
nonagon.................................9 sides
decagon.................................10 sides

To find the area of a polygon:
Rule—Multiply the sum of the sides (perimeter of the polygon) by the perpendicular dropped from its center to one of its sides, and half the product will be the area. This rule applies to all regular polygons.

To find the area of any regular polygon when the length of a side only is given:
Rule—Multiply the square of the sides by the figure for "Area when side = 1" opposite the polygon in Table 6-7.

Table 6-7. Table of Regular Polygons

Number of sides	3	4	5	6	7	8	9	10	11	12
Area when side = 1	.433	1.	1.721	2.598	3.634	4.828	6.181	7.694	9.366	11.196

The Circle

The Greek letter π (called pi) is used to represent 3.1416, the circumference of a circle whose diameter is 1. The circumference of a circle equals the diameter multiplied by 3.1416. The reason why the decimal .78543 is used to calculate the area of a circle is explained in Fig. 6-3.

To find the circumference of a circle:
Rule—Multiply the diameter by 3.1416.
To find the diameter of a circle (circumference given):
Rule—Divide the circumference by 3.1416.

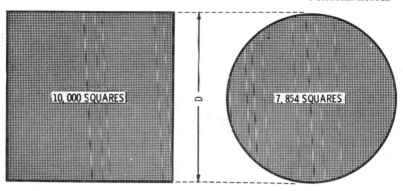

Fig. 6-3. Diagram illustrating why the decimal .7854 is used to find the area of a circle.

To find the area of a circle:
Rule—Multiply the square of the diameter by .7854. (See Fig. 6-3.)

To find the diameter of a circle (area given):
Rule—Extract the square root of the area divided by .7854.

To find the area of a sector of a circle:
Rule—Multiply the arc of the sector by half the radius.

To find the area of a segment of a circle:
Rule—Find the area of the sector which has the same arc and also the area of the triangle formed by the radii and chord; take the sum of these areas if the segment is greater than 1800; take the difference if less.

To find the area of a ring:
Rule—Take the difference between the areas of the two circles.

To find the area of an ellipse:
Rule—Multiply the product of the two diameters by .7854.

The following list shows the relation of a circle to an equal, inscribed, and circumscribed square.

Diameter of circle	× .88623	= side of equal square
Circumference of circle	× .28209	
Circumference of circle	× 1.1284	= perimeter of equal square

133

Diameter of circle	× .7071	
Circumference of		= side of inscribed
circle	× .22508	square
Area of circle	× .90031 ÷ diameter	
Area of circle	× 1.2732	= area of circum-scribed square
Area of circle	× .63662	= area of inscribed square
Side of square	× 1.4142	= diameter of circumscribed circle
Side of square	× 4.4428	= circumference
Side of square	× 1.1284	= diameter of equal circle
Side of square	× 3.5449	= circumference of equal circle
Perimeter of square	× .88623	= circumference of equal circle
Square inches	× 1.2732	= circular inches

Solids

Finding the volume of the solids involves the multiplication of three dimensions—length, breadth, and thickness.

To find the volume of a solid:
Rule—Multiply the area of the base by the perpendicular height.

To find the volume of a rectangular solid:
Rule—Multiply the length, breadth, and height.

To find the surface of a cylinder:
Rule—Multiply 3.1416 by the diameter times the length.

134

To find the volume of a cylinder:
Rule—Multiply .7854 by the diameter squared of the base times the length of the cylinder.

To find the surface of a sphere:
Rule—Multiply the area of its great circle by 4.

To find the volume of a sphere:
Rule—Multiply .7854 by the cube of the diameter, and then take ⅔ of the product.

To find the volume of a segment of a sphere:
Rule—To three times the square of the radius of the segment's base, add the square of the depth or height; then multiply this sum by the depth, and the product by .5236.

To find the surface of a cylindrical ring:
Rule—To the thickness of the ring, add the inner diameter; multiply this sum by the thickness, and the product again by 9.8696.

To find the volume of a cylindrical ring:
Rule—To the thickness of the ring, add the inner diameter; multiply this sum by the square of the thickness, and the product again by 2.4674.

To find the slant area of a cone:
Rule—Multiply 3.1416 by the diameter of the base and by one-half the slant height.

To find the slant area of the frustum of a cone:
Rule—Multiply half the slant height by the sum of the circumferences.

To find the volume of a cone:
Rule—Multiply the area of the base by the perpendicular height, and by ⅓.

To find the volume of a frustum of a cone:
Rule—Find the sum of the squares of the two diameters (d, D), and add to this the product of the two diameters multiplied by .7854, and by one-third the height (h).

To find the volume of a pyramid:
Rule—Multiply the area of the base by one-third of the perpendicular height.

To find the volume of rectangular solid:
Rule—Multiply the length, breadth, and thickness.

To find the volume of a rectangular wedge:

Rule—Find the area of one of the triangle ends and multiply by the distance between ends.

Mensuration of Surfaces and Volumes

Area of rectangle = length × breadth.
Area of triangle = base × ½ perpendicular height.
Diameter of circle = radius × 2.
Circumference of circle = diameter × 3.1416.
Area of circle = square of diameter × .7854.
Area of sector of circle =

$$\frac{\text{area of circle} \times \text{number of degrees in arc}}{360}$$

Area of surface of cylinder = circumference × length + area of two ends.

To find diameter of circle having given area: Divide the area by .7854, and extract the square root.

To find the volume of a cylinder: Multiply the area of the section in square inches by the length in inches = the volume in cubic inches. Cubic inches divided by 1728 = volume in cubic feet.

Surface of a sphere = square of diameter × 3.1416.
Volume of a sphere = cube of diameter × .5236.
Side of an inscribed cube = radius of a sphere × 1.1547.

Area of the base of a pyramid or cone, whether round, square or triangular, multiplied by one-third of its height = the volume.

Diameter × .8862 = side of an equal square.
Diameter × .7071 = side of an inscribed square.
Radius × 6.2832 = circumference.
Circumference = 3.5446 × $\sqrt{\text{Area of circle}}$.
Diameter = 1.1283 × $\sqrt{\text{Area of circle}}$.
Length of arc = No. of degrees × .017453 radius.
Degrees in arc whose length equals radius = 57° 2958′.
Length of an arc of 1° = radius × .017453.
Length of an arc of 1 min. = radius × .0002909.
Length of an arc of 1 sec. = radius × .0000048.

π = Proportion of circumference to diameter = 3.1415926.

π^2 = 9.8696044.

$\sqrt{\pi}$ = 1.7724538.

Logπ = 0.49715.

$\dfrac{1}{\pi}$ = 0.31831.

1/360 = .002778.

$\dfrac{360}{\pi}$ = 114.59.

Lineal feet	× .00019	= Miles.
Lineal yards	× .0006	= Miles.
Square inches	× .007	= Square feet.
Square feet	× .111	= Square yards.
Square yards	× .0002067	= Acres.
Acres	× 4840.	= Square yards.
Cubic inches	× .00058	= Cubic feet.
Cubic feet	× .03704	= Cubic yards.
Circular inches	× .00546	= Square feet.
Cyl. inches	× .0004546	= Cubic feet.
Cyl. feet	× .02909	= Cubic yards.
Links	× .22	= Yards.
Links	× .66	= Feet.
Feet	× 1.5	= Links.
Width in chains	× 8	= Acres per mile.
Cubic feet	× 7.48	= U.S. gallons.
Cubic inches	× .004329	= U.S. gallons.
U.S. gallons	× .13367	= Cubic feet.
U.S. gallons	× 231	= Cubic inches.
Cubic feet	× .8036	= U.S. bushel.
Cubic inches	× .000466	= U.S. bushel.
Lbs. Avoir	× .009	= Cwt. (112)
Lbs. Avoir	× .00045	= Tons (2240)
Cubic feet of water	× 62.5	= Lbs. Avoir.
Cubic inch of water	× .03617	= Lbs. Avoir.
13.44 U.S. gallons of water		= 1 cwt.
268.8 U.S. gallons of water		= 1 ton.
1.8 cubic feet of water		= 1 cwt.
35.88 cubic feet of water		= 1 ton.
Column of water, 12 inches high, and 1 inch in diameter		= .341 lbs.
U.S. bushel	× .0495	= Cubic yards.
U.S. bushel	× 1.2446	= Cubic feet.
U.S. bushel	× 150.42	= Cubic inches.

137

To find the volume of irregular solids.

Rule—Divide the irregular solid into different figures; and the sum of their volumes, found by the preceding problems, will be the volume required. If the figure is a compound solid, whose two ends are equal plane figures, the volume may be found by multiplying the area of one end by the length. To find the volume of a piece of wood or stone that is craggy or uneven, put it into a tub or cistern, and pour in as much water as will just cover it; then take it out and find the contents of that part of the vessel through which the water has descended and it will be the volume required.

To find the surface and volume of any of the five regular solids shown in Fig. 6-4.

Rule—(surface) Multiply the area given in Table 6-8 by the square of the edge of the solid.

Rule—(volume) Multiply the contents given in Table 6-8 by the cube of the given edge.

Fig. 6-4. The five regular solids.

Table 6-8. Surfaces and Volumes of Regular Solids

Number of Sides	Name	Area Edge =	Contents Edge = 1
4	Tetrahedron	1.7320	0.1178
6	Hexahedron	6.0000	1.0000
8	Octahedron....................	3.4641	0.4714
12	Dodecahedron	20.6458	7.6631
20	Icosahedron	8.6603	2.1817

TRIGONOMETRIC FUNCTIONS

Every triangle has only six parts—3 sides and 3 angles. When any three of these parts are given (provided one of them is a side), the other parts may be determined. Fig. 6-5 illustrates the parts consid-

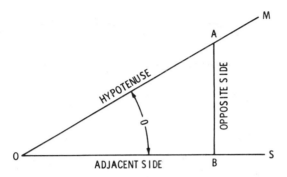

Fig. 6-5. A triangle, AOB, for expressing trigonometric functions as ratios.

ered in expressing trigonometric functions. It will be noted in this triangle that angle ABO = 90°. In this triangle the trigonometric functions, expressed as ratios, are as follows:

$$\text{Sine of the angle} = \frac{AB}{AO} = \frac{\text{opposite side}}{\text{hypotenuse}}$$

$$\text{Cosine of the angle} = \frac{OB}{OA} = \frac{\text{adjacent side}}{\text{hypotenuse}}$$

$$\text{Tangent of the angle} = \frac{AB}{OB} = \frac{\text{opposite side}}{\text{adjacent side}}$$

$$\text{Cotangent of the angle} = \frac{OB}{AB} = \frac{\text{adjacent side}}{\text{opposite side}}$$

$$\text{Secant of the angle} = \frac{OA}{OB} = \frac{\text{hypotenuse}}{\text{adjacent side}}$$

$$\text{Cosecant of the angle} = \frac{OA}{AB} = \frac{\text{hypotenuse}}{\text{opposite side}}$$

Natural Functions

These are virtually ratios, but by taking what corresponds to the hypotenuse OA, in the triangle AOB in Fig. 6-5, as a radius of unity length of a circle, the denominators of the ratios are unity or 1. These denominators disappear, leaving only the numerators; that is, a line instead of a ratio or function. These lines are the so-called *natural functions*. Thus, in Fig. 6-6:

$$Sine\ angle\ =\ \frac{AB}{radius}\ =\ \frac{AB}{1}\ =\ AB$$

$$Cosine\ angle\ =\ \frac{radius}{OB}\ =\ OB$$

$$Tangent\ angle\ =\ \frac{MS}{OS}\ =\ \frac{MS}{radius}\ =\ MS$$

Cotangent angle = tangent of complement of angle

$$=\ \frac{OM}{OF}\ =\ \frac{OM}{radius}\ =\ OM$$

$$Secant\ angle\ =\ \frac{OM}{OS}\ =\ \frac{OM}{radius}\ =\ OM$$

Cosecant angle = secant of complement angle =

$$\frac{OL}{OF}\ =\ \frac{OL}{radius}\ =\ OL$$

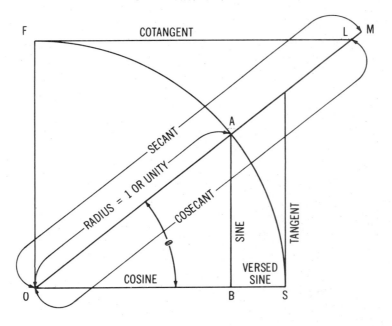

Fig. 6-6. Natural trigonometric functions.

The natural trigonometric functions shown in Fig. 6-7 are the ones of value in ordinary calculations and should be thoroughly understood. They are used in connection with Table 6-9, as illustrated by the following example.

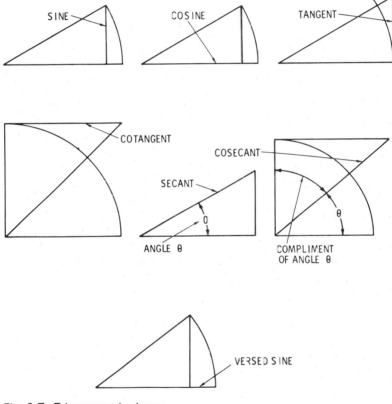

Fig. 6-7. Trigonometric shapes.

Example—In Fig. 6-8, two pipe lines 8 in. apart are to be connected with 30° elbows. What is the length of the offset OB and connecting pipe OA? From Table 6-9, tangent 60° = 1.73; length offset OB = 1.73 × 8 = 13.84. Again, from Table 6-9, secant 60° = 2; length connecting pipe OA = 8 × 2 = 16 ins.

It is often necessary to figure the capacity of a round storage tank. The old standard methods involve several steps; the more

141

Table 6-9. Natural Trigonometric Functions

Degs.	Sine	Cosine	Tangent	Secant	Degs.	Sine	Cosine	Tangent	Secant
0	0.00000	1.0000	0.00000	1.0000	46	0.7193	0.6947	1.0355	1.4395
1	0.01745	0.9998	0.01745	1.0001	47	0.7314	0.6820	1.0724	1.4663
2	0.03490	0.9994	0.03492	1.0006	48	0.7431	0.6691	1.1106	1.4945
3	0.05234	0.9986	0.05241	1.0014	49	0.7547	0.6561	1.1504	1.5242
4	0.06976	0.9976	0.06993	1.0024	50	0.7660	0.6428	1.1918	1.5557
5	0.08716	0.9962	0.08749	1.0038	51	0.7771	0.6293	1.2349	1.5890
6	0.10453	0.9945	0.10510	1.0055	52	0.7880	0.6157	1.2799	1.6243
7	0.12187	0.9925	0.12278	1.0075	53	0.7986	0.6018	1.3270	1.6616
8	0.1392	0.9903	0.1405	1.0098	54	0.8090	0.5878	1.3764	1.7013
9	0.1564	0.9877	0.1584	1.0125	55	0.8192	0.5736	1.4281	1.7434
10	0.1736	0.9848	0.1763	1.0154	56	0.8290	0.5592	1.4826	1.7883
11	0.1908	0.9816	0.1944	1.0187	57	0.8387	0.5446	1.5399	1.8361
12	0.2079	0.9781	0.2126	1.0223	58	0.8480	0.5299	1.6003	1.8871
13	0.2250	0.9744	0.2309	1.0263	59	0.8572	0.5150	1.6643	1.9416
14	0.2419	0.9703	0.2493	1.0306	60	0.8660	0.5000	1.7321	2.0000
15	0.2588	0.9659	0.2679	1.0353	61	0.8746	0.4848	1.8040	2.0627
16	0.2756	0.9613	0.2867	1.0403	62	0.8829	0.4695	1.8807	2.1300
17	0.2924	0.9563	0.3057	1.0457	63	0.8910	0.4540	1.9626	2.2027
18	0.3090	0.9511	0.3249	1.0515	64	0.8988	0.4384	2.0503	2.2812
19	0.3256	0.9455	0.3443	1.0576	65	0.9063	0.4226	2.1445	2.3662
20	0.3420	0.9397	0.3640	1.0642	66	0.9135	0.4067	2.2460	2.4586
21	0.3584	0.9336	0.3839	1.0711	67	0.9205	0.3907	2.3559	2.5593
22	0.3746	0.9272	0.4040	1.0785	68	0.9272	0.3746	2.4751	2.6695
23	0.3907	0.9205	0.4245	1.0864	69	0.9336	0.3584	2.6051	2.7904
24	0.4067	0.9135	0.4452	1.0946	70	0.9397	0.3420	2.7475	2.9238
25	0.4226	0.9063	0.4663	1.1034	71	0.9455	0.3256	2.9042	3.0715
26	0.4384	0.8988	0.4877	1.1126	72	0.9511	0.3090	3.0777	3.2361
27	0.4540	0.8910	0.5095	1.1223	73	0.9563	0.2924	3.2709	3.4203
28	0.4695	0.8829	0.5317	1.1326	74	0.9613	0.2756	3.4874	3.6279
29	0.4848	0.8746	0.5543	1.1433	75	0.9659	0.2588	3.7321	3.8637
30	0.5000	0.8660	0.5774	1.1547	76	0.9703	0.2419	4.0108	4.1336
31	0.5150	0.8572	0.6009	1.1666	77	0.9744	0.2250	4.3315	4.4454
32	0.5299	0.8480	0.6249	1.1792	78	0.9781	0.2079	4.7046	4.8097
33	0.5446	0.8387	0.6494	1.1924	79	0.9816	0.1908	5.1446	5.2408
34	0.5592	0.8290	0.6745	1.2062	80	0.9848	0.1736	5.6713	5.7588
35	0.5736	0.8192	0.7002	1.2208	81	0.9877	0.1564	6.3138	6.3924
36	0.5878	0.8090	0.7265	1.2361	82	0.9903	0.1392	7.1154	7.1853
37	0.6018	0.7986	0.7536	1.2521	83	0.9925	0.12187	8.1443	8.2055
38	0.6157	0.7880	0.7813	1.2690	84	0.9945	0.10453	9.5144	9.5668
39	0.6293	0.7771	0.8098	1.2867	85	0.9962	0.08716	11.4301	11.474
40	0.6428	0.7660	0.8391	1.3054	86	0.9976	0.06976	14.3007	14.335
41	0.6561	0.7547	0.8693	1.3250	87	0.9986	0.05234	19.0811	19.107
42	0.6691	0.7431	0.9004	1.3456	88	0.9994	0.03490	28.6363	28.654
43	0.6820	0.7314	0.9325	1.3673	89	0.9998	0.01745	57.2900	57.299
44	0.6947	0.7193	0.9657	1.3902	90	1.0000	Inf.	Inf.	Inf.
45	0.7071	0.7071	1.0000	1.4142					

steps used, the greater the possibility of error. Newer, simpler methods of computing tank capacities reduce the possibility of errors. A comparison of the two methods follows.

Old method—tank measured in inches

formula: $D^2 \times .7854 \times L \div 231$ = gallons

Example: How many gallons are in a tank 12 in. in diameter and 60 in. long?

Solution:

12	144	113.0976	29.3760
× 12	× .7854	× 60	231)6785.856
144	576	6785.856	462
	720		2165
	1152		2079
	1008		868
	113.0976		693
			1755
			1617
			1386
			1386
			0000

Answer: 29.3760 gallons in tank.

New method—tank measured in inches.

formula: $D^2 \times L \times .0034$ = gallons

Example: How many gallons are in a tank 12 in. in diameter and 60 in. long?

Solution:

12	144	8640
× 12	× 60	× .0034
144	8640	34560
		25920
		29.3760

Answer: 29.3760 gallons in tank.

Old method—tank measured in feet.

formula: $D^2 \times .7854 \times L \times 7.5$ = gallons

143

Example: How many gallons are in a tank 1 ft. in diameter and 5 ft. long?

Solution:

1	.7854	.7854	3.9270
× 1	× 1	× 5	× 7.5
1	.7854	3.9270	19635
			27489
			29.4525

Answer: 29.4525 gallons.

NOTE: Using the old standard methods, there is a slight difference in the answers.

New method, using a combination of feet and inches;

formula: $D^2 \times L \times .0408$

Example: How many gallons are in a tank 12 in. in diameter and 5 ft. long?

Solution:

12	144	720
× 12	× 5	.0408
144	720	5760
		28800
		29.3760

Answer: 29.3760 gallons in tank.

NOTE: The simplicity of the new methods is readily apparent, and the answers are virtually identical.

One of the most common problems in plumbers' mathematics is to figure the length of pipe when making a common offset in a piping run. Changes in direction using simple offsets are made by using elbows or in some cases, wyes, where a cleanout fitting is desirable. The angle of the fitting is the number of degrees in the change of direction. Thus a 45° elbow changes the direction 45°. Fig. 6-9 shows the terms used for various parts of an offset. There are some simple formulas which can be used to calculate offsets. These formulas or multipliers are shown in Table 6-10.

Example: If the set, S, is 12 in. then to find the travel, T, using 45° elbows, Table 6-10, shows that the multiplier for 45° offsets

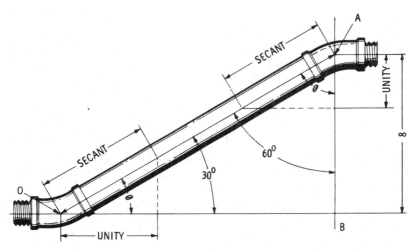

Fig. 6-8. Two parallel pipe lines connected with 30° elbows illustrating the use of natural trigonometric functions in finding the offset and length of connecting pipes.

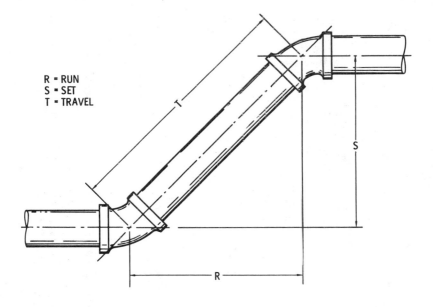

R = RUN
S = SET
T = TRAVEL

Fig. 6-9. Terms used for various parts of an offset.

145

Table 6-10. Constants for Measuring Offsets in Piping

known side	to find side	multiply side	using 5⅝ ell	using 11¼ ell	using 22½ ell	using 30 ell	using 45 ell	using 60 ell
S	T	S	10.19	5.13	2.61	2.00	1.41	1.15
S	R	S	10.16	5.03	2.41	1.73	1.00	.58
R	S	R	.10	.20	.41	.58	1.00	1.73
R	T	R	1.00	1.02	1.08	1.16	1.41	2.00
T	S	T	.10	.20	.38	.50	.71	.87
T	R	T	1.00	.98	.92	.87	.71	.50

Table 6-11. Area of Circles

Diam-eter	Area	Diam-eter	Area	Diam-eter	Area	Diam-eter	Area
⅛	0.0123	10	78.54	30	706.86	65	3318.3
¼	0.0491	10½	86.59	31	754.77	66	3421.2
⅜	0.1105	11	95.03	32	804.25	67	3525.7
½	0.1964	11½	103.87	33	855.30	68	3631.7
⅝	0.3068	12	113.09	34	907.92	69	3739.3
¾	0.4418	12½	122.72	35	962.11	70	3848.5
⅞	0.6013	13	132.73	36	1017.9	71	3959.2
1	0.7854	13½	143.14	37	1075.2	72	4071.5
1⅛	0.9940	14	153.94	38	1134.1	73	4185.4
1¼	1.227	14½	165.13	39	1194.6	74	4300.8
1⅜	1.485	15	176.71	40	1256.6	75	4417.9
1½	1.767	15½	188.69	41	1320.3	76	4536.5
1⅝	2.079	16	201.06	42	1385.4	77	4656.6
1¾	2.405	16½	213.82	43	1452.2	78	4778.4
1⅞	2.761	17	226.98	44	1520.5	79	4901.7
2	3.142	17½	240.53	45	1590.4	80	5026.5
2¼	3.976	18	254.47	46	1661.9	81	5153.0
2½	4.909	18½	268.80	47	1734.9	82	5281.0
2¾	5.940	19	283.53	48	1809.6	83	5410.6
3	7.069	19½	298.65	49	1885.7	84	5541.8
3¼	8.296	20	314.16	50	1963.5	85	5674.5
3½	9.621	20½	330.06	51	2042.8	86	5808.8
3¾	11.045	21	346.36	52	2123.7	87	5944.7
4	12.566	21½	363.05	53	2206.2	88	6082.1
4½	15.904	22	380.13	54	2290.2	89	6221.1
5	19.635	22½	397.61	55	2375.8	90	6361.7
5½	23.758	23	415.48	56	2463.0	91	6503.9
6	28.274	23½	433.74	57	2551.8	92	6647.6
6½	33.183	24	452.39	58	2642.1	93	6792.9
7	38.485	24½	471.44	59	2734.0	94	6939.8
7½	44.179	25	490.87	60	2827.4	95	7088.2
8	50.265	26	530.93	61	2922.5	96	7238.2
8½	56.745	27	572.56	62	3019.1	97	7389.8
9	63.617	28	615.75	63	3117.2	98	7543.0
9½	70.882	29	660.52	64	3217.0	99	7697.7

Table 6-12. Circumference of Circles

Diam-eter	Circumfer-ence	Diam-eter	Circumfer-ence	Diam-eter	Circumfer-ence	Diam-eter	Circumfer-ence
1/8	.3927	10	31.42	30	94.25	65	204.2
1/4	.7854	10½	32.99	31	97.39	66	207.3
3/8	1.178	11	34.56	32	100.5	67	210.5
1/2	1.571	11½	36.13	33	103.7	68	213.6
5/8	1.963	12	37.70	34	106.8	69	216.8
3/4	2.356	12½	39.27	35	110.0	70	219.9
7/8	2.749	13	40.84	36	113.1	71	223.0
1	3.142	13½	42.41	37	116.2	72	226.2
1⅛	3.534	14	43.98	38	119.4	73	229.3
1¼	3.927	14½	45.55	39	122.5	74	232.5
1⅜	4.320	15	47.12	40	125.7	75	235.6
1½	4.712	15½	48.69	41	128.8	76	238.8
1⅝	5.105	16	50.26	42	131.9	77	241.9
1¾	5.498	16½	51.84	43	135.1	78	245.0
1⅞	5.890	17	53.41	44	138.2	79	248.2
2	6.283	17½	54.98	45	141.4	80	251.3
2¼	7.069	18	56.55	46	144.5	81	254.5
2½	7.854	18½	58.12	47	147.7	82	257.6
2¾	8.639	19	59.69	48	150.8	83	260.8
3	9.425	19½	61.26	49	153.9	84	263.9
3¼	10.21	20	62.83	50	157.1	85	267.0
3½	11.00	20½	64.40	51	160.2	86	270.2
3¾	11.78	21	65.97	52	163.4	87	273.3
4	12.57	21½	67.54	53	166.5	88	276.5
4½	14.14	22	69.12	54	169.6	89	279.6
5	15.71	22½	70.69	55	172.8	90	282.7
5½	17.28	23	72.26	56	175.9	91	285.9
6	18.85	23½	73.83	57	179.1	92	289.0
6½	20.42	24	75.40	58	182.2	93	292.2
7	21.99	24½	76.97	59	185.4	94	295.3
7½	23.56	25	78.54	60	188.5	95	298.5
8	25.13	26	81.68	61	191.6	96	301.6
8½	26.70	27	84.82	62	194.8	97	304.7
9	28.27	28	87.96	63	197.9	98	307.9
9½	29.84	29	91.11	64	201.1	99	311.0

Table 6-13. Logarithms of Numbers

No.	0	1	2	3	4	5	6	7	8	9	Diff.
10	00000	00432	00860	01284	01703	02119	02531	02938	03342	03743	415
11	04139	04532	04922	05308	05690	06070	06446	06819	07188	07555	379
12	07918	08279	08636	08991	09342	09691	10037	10380	10721	11059	344
13	11394	11727	12057	12385	12710	13033	13354	13672	13988	14301	323
14	14613	14922	15229	15534	15836	16137	16435	16732	17026	17319	298
15	17609	17898	18184	18469	18752	19033	19312	19590	19866	20140	281
16	20412	20683	20952	21219	21484	21748	22011	22272	22531	22789	264
17	23045	23300	23553	23805	24055	24304	24551	24797	25042	25285	249
18	25527	25768	26007	26245	26482	26717	26951	27184	27416	27646	234
19	27875	28103	28330	28556	28780	29003	29226	29447	29667	29885	222
20	30103	30320	30535	30750	30963	31175	31387	31597	31806	32015	212
21	32222	32428	32634	32838	33041	33244	33445	33646	33846	34044	202
22	34242	34439	34635	34830	35025	35218	35411	35603	35793	35984	193
23	36173	36361	36549	36736	36922	37107	37291	37475	37658	37840	185
24	38021	38202	38382	38561	38739	38917	39094	39270	39445	39620	177
25	39794	39967	40140	40312	40483	40654	40824	40993	41162	41330	170
26	41497	41664	41830	41996	42160	42325	42488	42651	42813	42975	164
27	43136	43297	43457	43616	43775	43933	44091	44248	44404	44560	158
28	44716	44871	45025	45179	45332	45484	45637	45788	45939	46090	153
29	46240	46389	46538	46687	46835	46982	47129	47276	47422	47567	148
30	47712	47857	48001	48144	48287	48430	48572	48714	48855	48996	143
31	49136	49276	49415	49554	49693	49831	49969	50160	50243	50379	138
32	50515	50651	50786	50920	51055	51189	51322	51455	51587	51720	134
33	51851	51983	52114	52244	52375	52504	52634	52763	52892	53020	130
34	53148	53275	53403	53529	53656	53782	53908	54033	54158	54283	126
35	54407	54531	54654	54777	54900	55023	55145	55267	55388	55509	122
36	55630	55751	55871	55991	56110	56229	56348	56467	56585	56703	119
37	56820	56937	57054	57171	57287	57403	57519	57634	57749	57864	116
38	57978	58093	58206	58320	58433	58546	58659	58771	58883	58995	113
39	59106	59218	59329	59439	59550	59660	59770	59879	59988	60097	110
40	60206	60314	60423	60531	60638	60746	60853	60959	61066	61172	107
41	61278	61384	61490	61595	61700	61805	61909	62014	62118	62221	104
42	62325	62428	62531	62634	62737	62839	62941	63043	63144	63246	102
43	63347	63448	63548	63649	63749	63849	63949	64048	64147	64246	99
44	64345	64444	64542	64640	64738	64836	64933	65031	65128	65225	98
45	65321	65418	65514	65610	65706	65801	65896	65992	66087	66181	96
46	66276	66370	66464	66558	66652	66745	66839	66932	67025	67117	95
47	67210	67302	67394	67486	67578	67669	67761	67852	67943	68034	92
48	68124	68215	68305	68395	68485	68574	68664	68753	68842	68931	90
49	69020	69108	69197	69285	69373	69461	69548	69636	69723	69810	88
50	69897	69984	70070	70157	70243	70329	70415	70501	70586	70672	86
51	70757	70842	70927	71012	71096	71181	71265	71349	71433	71517	84
52	71600	71684	71767	71852	71933	72016	72099	72181	72263	72346	82
53	72428	72509	72591	72673	72754	72835	72916	72997	73078	73159	81
54	73239	73320	73400	73480	73560	73640	73719	73799	73878	73957	80

Table 6-13. Logarithms of Numbers (Cont'd)

No.	0	1	2	3	4	5	6	7	8	9	Diff.
55	74036	74115	74194	74273	74351	74429	74507	74586	74663	74741	78
56	74819	74896	74974	75051	75128	75205	75282	75358	75435	75511	77
57	75587	75664	75740	75815	75891	75967	76042	76118	76193	76268	75
58	76343	76418	76492	76567	76641	76716	76790	76864	76938	77012	74
59	77085	77159	77232	77305	77379	77452	77525	77597	77670	77743	73
60	77815	77887	77960	78032	78104	78176	78247	78319	78390	78462	72
61	78533	78604	78675	78746	78817	78888	78958	79029	79099	79169	71
62	79239	79309	79379	79449	79518	79588	79657	79727	79796	79865	70
63	79934	80003	80072	80140	80209	80277	80346	80414	80482	80550	69
64	80618	80686	80754	80821	80889	80956	81023	81090	81158	81224	68
65	81291	81358	81425	81491	81558	81624	81690	81757	81823	81889	67
66	81954	82020	82086	82151	82217	82282	82347	82413	82478	82543	66
67	82607	82672	82737	82802	82866	82930	82995	83059	83123	83187	64
68	83251	83315	83378	83442	83506	83569	83632	83696	83759	83822	63
69	83885	83948	84011	84073	84136	84198	84261	84323	84386	84448	63
70	84510	84572	84634	84696	84757	84819	84880	84942	85003	85065	62
71	85126	85187	85248	85309	85370	85431	85491	85552	85612	85673	61
72	85733	85794	85854	85914	85974	86034	86094	86153	86213	86273	60
73	86332	86392	86451	86510	86570	86629	86688	86747	86806	86864	59
74	86923	86982	87040	87099	87157	87216	87274	87332	87390	87448	58
75	87506	87564	87622	87680	87737	87795	87852	87910	87967	88024	57
76	88081	88138	88196	88252	88309	88366	88423	88480	88536	88593	57
77	88649	88705	88762	88818	88874	88930	88986	89042	89098	89154	56
78	89209	89265	89321	89376	89432	89487	89542	89597	89653	89708	55
79	89763	89818	89873	89927	89982	90037	90091	90146	90200	90255	54
80	90309	90363	90417	90472	90526	90580	90634	90687	90741	90795	54
81	90849	90902	90956	91009	91062	91116	91169	91222	91275	91328	53
82	91381	91434	91487	91540	91593	91645	91698	91751	91803	91855	53
83	91908	91960	92012	92065	92117	92169	92221	92273	92324	92376	52
84	92428	92480	92531	92583	92634	92686	92737	92788	92840	92891	51
85	92942	92993	93044	93095	93146	93197	93247	93298	93349	93399	51
86	93450	93500	93551	93601	93651	93702	93752	93802	93852	93902	50
87	93952	94002	94052	94101	94151	94201	94250	94300	94349	94399	49
88	94448	94498	94547	94596	94645	94694	94743	94792	94841	94890	49
89	94939	94988	95036	95085	95134	95182	95231	95279	95328	95376	48
90	95424	95472	95521	95569	95617	95665	95713	95761	95809	95856	48
91	95904	95952	95999	96047	96095	96142	96190	96237	96284	96332	48
92	96379	96426	96473	96520	96567	96614	96661	96708	96755	96802	47
93	96848	96895	96942	96988	97035	97081	97128	97174	97220	97267	47
94	97313	97359	97405	97451	97497	97543	97589	97635	97681	97727	46
95	97772	97818	97864	97909	97955	98000	98046	98091	98137	98182	46
96	98227	98272	98318	98363	98408	98453	98498	98543	98588	98632	45
97	98677	98722	98767	98811	98856	98900	98945	98989	99034	99078	45
98	99123	99167	99211	99255	99300	99344	99388	99432	99476	99520	44
99	99564	99607	99651	99695	99739	99782	99826	99870	99913	99957	44

149

is 1.41. Multiplying 12 $\times$ 1.41 shows that the travel, T, is 16.92 in. Rounding this off, $T = 17.00$ in. Table 6-10 is very useful when figuring offsets using standard fittings.

MATHEMATICAL TABLES

Tables 6-11, 6-12, and 6-13 are for convenient reference and will be found useful in numerous calculations.

CHAPTER 7

Physics for Plumbers
and Pipe Fitters

By definition, physics is *the science or group of sciences that treats of the phenomena associated with matter in general, especially in its relations to energy, and of the laws governing these phenomena, excluding the special laws and phenomena peculiar to living matter (biology) or to special kinds of matter (chemistry).*
Physics is generally considered to treat of:

1. The constitution and properties of matter.
2. Mechanics.
3. Acoustics.
4. Heat.
5. Optics.
6. Electricity and magnetism.

As sometimes used in a limited sense, physics embraces only the last four divisions; more generally, it includes all the physical sciences.

According to Barker, physics regards matter solely as the vehicle of energy. From this point of view, physics may be defined as *that department of science whose province it is to investigate all those phenomena of nature that depend either upon the transference of energy from one portion of matter to another, or upon its transformation into any of the forms it is capable of assuming.* In a word, physics may be regarded as the science of energy, precisely as chemistry may be regarded as the science of matter.

The scope of physics extends considerably beyond what is important to the plumber. Only relevant subjects will be presented here. In this connection, the plumber should thoroughly study this chapter, and should understand not only such things as why pipes burst in freezing weather or why water circulates in hot-water heating systems, but should know the reasons for all the various phenomena commonly observed at work. For instance, he should know why pipes become air bound; why air chambers on pumps fill with water; why a boiler water gauge does not register the true water level; why a bucket-valve pump delivers more than its displacement; etc.

MEASUREMENTS

According to Plato, physics begins with measurements. In fact, if arithmetic, mensuration, and weighing are taken away from any art, that which remains will not be much.

There are three fundamental kinds of measurements:

1. Length.
2. Mass.
3. Time.

In addition to these, there are *derived* measurements of:

1. Area.
2. Volume.

These are called *derived* because they are the products of two and three lengths. Various units are used for these measurements.

The plumber uses the ordinary unit such as inches, pounds, and seconds for fundamental measurements, and uses square inches and cubic inches for derived measurements. In addition to measuring the size or weight of an object, other measurements are necessary in physics, such as the measurement of pressure and temperature. Such measurements are indicated by instruments provided with arbitrary scales divided into standard divisions, each division standing for a unit of pressure, temperature, etc.

Most commonly used for measurement are the wood folding rule (Fig. 7-1) and the steel tape. The steel tape (Fig. 7-2) is enclosed, as the name implies, in a metal case with the measuring tape folding into the device for ease of carrying and use. Both the folding and tape rule are usually six feet long, although many of the steel tapes are available in eight- and ten-foot lengths, making floor-to-ceiling measurements much easier.

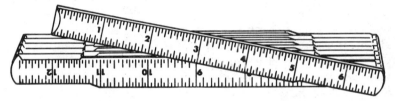

Fig. 7-1. A common six-foot folding rule.

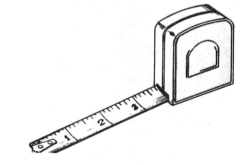

Fig. 7-2. Steel tape.

WATER

Water is a *compound of hydrogen and oxygen in the proportion of 2 parts by weight of hydrogen to 16 parts by weight of oxygen.*

Since the atom of oxygen is believed to weigh 16 times as much as the atom of hydrogen, the molecule of water is said to contain 2 atoms of hydrogen and 1 atom of oxygen, being represented by the formula H_2O.

Under the influence of temperature and pressure, this substance (H_2O) may exist as:

1. A solid.
2. A liquid.
3. A gas.

As a solid, it is called *ice;* as a liquid, *water;* as a gas, *steam.* Water at its maximum density (39.1° F) will expand as heat is added, and it will also expand slightly as the temperature falls from this point, as illustrated in Fig. 7-3. Water will freeze at 32° F and boil at 212° F, when the barometer reads 29.921 in. of mercury.

The boiling point of water is not the same in all places. It decreases as the altitude increases; at an altitude of 5,000 ft., water will boil at a temperature of 202° F. An increase of pressure will elevate the boiling point of water. At maximum density, the weight of a cu. ft. of water is generally taken as 62.425 lbs. One U.S. gallon (231 cu. in.) of water weighs 8⅓ lbs. The figure 8⅓ is correct when the water is at a temperature of 65° F. The pressure

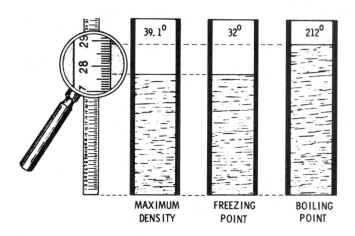

MAXIMUM   FREEZING   BOILING
DENSITY   POINT   POINT

Fig. 7-3. The effect of water at various temperatures.

of water varies with the head, and is equal to .43302 lbs. per sq. in. for every foot of (static) head.

HEAT

By definition, heat *is a form of energy known by its effects.* These effects are indicated through touch and feel as well as by the expansion, fusion, combustion, or evaporation of the matter upon which it acts. Temperature is that which indicates how hot or cold a substance is; a measure of *sensible heat.*

Sensible heat is that heat which produces a rise of temperature as distinguished from latent heat. *Latent heat* is that quantity of heat required to change the *state* or condition under which a substance exists without changing its temperature. Thus, a definite quantity of heat must be transferred to ice at 32° to change it into water at the same temperature.

Specific heat is the ratio of the quantity of heat required to raise the temperature of a given weight of any substance one degree to the quantity of heat required to raise the temperature of the same weight of water from 62° to 63° F. When bodies of unequal temperatures are placed near each other, heat leaves the hot body and is absorbed by the colder body until the temperature of each is equal. This is called a transfer of heat.

The rate by which the heat is absorbed by the colder body is proportional to the difference of temperature between the two bodies. The greater the difference of temperature, the greater the rate of flow of the heat. The transfer of heat takes place by radiation, conduction, or convection. Thus, in a boiler, heat is given off from the furnace fire in rays which radiate in straight lines in all directions, being transferred to the crown and sides of the furnace by radiation; it passes through the plates by conduction, and is transferred to the water by convection (that is, by currents).

Bodies expand by the action of heat. For instance, boiler plates are riveted with red-hot rivets in an expanded state; on cooling, the rivets contract and draw the plates together with great force, making a tight joint. An exception to the rule, it should be noted, is water, which contracts as it is heated from the freezing point 32° F,

155

to the point of maximum density at 39.1°; at other temperatures it
expands.

HEAT AND WORK

Heat develops *mechanical force* and *motion;* hence, it is *convertible into mechanical work.* Heat is measured by a standard unit called the British unit of heat. The *British thermal unit* is equal to $\frac{1}{180}$ of the heat required to raise the temperature of one pound of water from 32° to 212° F. It should be noted that this is the definition adapted in this work for the British thermal unit (Btu), corresponding to the unit used in the Marks and Davis steam tables, which is now the recognized standard.

WORK

By definition, work is *the overcoming of resistance through a certain distance by the expenditure of energy.* Work is measured by a standard unit called the *foot pound.* A foot pound is *the amount of work done in raising one pound one foot,* or in overcoming a pressure of one pound through a distance of one foot. Thus, if a 5-pound weight is raised 10 feet, the work done is $5 \times 10 = 50$ feet pounds.

JOULE'S EXPERIMENT

It was shown by experiments made by Joule in 1843-50 that 1 *unit of heat* = 772 *units of work.* This is known as the *mechanical equivalent of heat,* or Joule's equivalent.

Experiments by Prof. Rowland (1880) and others, give higher figures; 778 is generally accepted, but 777.5 is probably more nearly correct, the value 777.52 being used by Marks and Davis in their steam tables. The value 778 is sufficiently accurate for ordinary calculations.

156

ENERGY

By definition. *energy is stored work;* that is, the ability to do work, or in other words, to move against resistance. A body may possess energy whether it does any work or not, but no work is ever done except by the expenditure of energy. There are two kinds of energy.:

1. Potential.
2. Kinetic.

Potential energy is energy due to position, as represented for instance, by a body of water stored in an elevated reservoir, and capable of doing work by means of a water wheel.

Kinetic energy is energy due to momentum; that is, the energy of a moving body.

Conservation of Energy

The doctrine of physics is that energy can be transmitted from one body to another or transformed in its manifestations, but *may neither be created nor destroyed.*

POWER

By definition, power is the *rate* at which work is done; in other words, it is work divided by the *time* in which it is done. The unit of power in general use is the *horsepower*, which is defined as 33,000 foot pounds per minute. One horsepower is required to raise a weight of:

33,000 pounds	1 foot in one minute
3300 pounds	10 feet in one minute
330 pounds	100 feet in one minute
33 pounds	1000 feet in one minute
3.3 pounds	10,000 feet in one minute
1 pound	33,000 feet in one minute, etc.

157

PRESSURE

By definition, pressure is *a force, in the nature of a thrust, distributed over a surface;* in other words, the kind of force with which a body tends to expand, or resist an effort to compress it. Pressure is usually stated in pounds per square inch, meaning that a pressure of a given number of pounds is distributed over each square inch of surface. This should be very clearly understood as further explained in Fig. 7-4.

Atmospheric pressure is the force exerted by the weight of the atmosphere on every point with which it is in contact. At sea level, this pressure is taken at 14.7 pounds per sq. in. for ordinary calculations. We do not feel the atmospheric pressure because air presses the body both externally and internally so that the pressure in different directions balance. Atmospheric pressure varies with the elevation. The pressure decreases approximately one-half pound

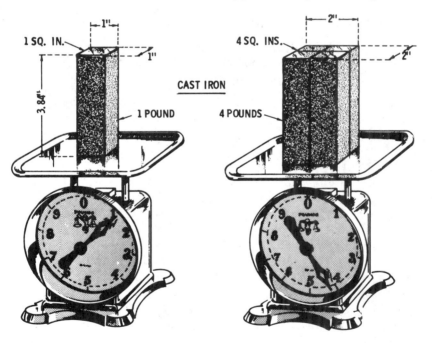

Fig. 7-4. Pressure per square inch.

for every 1000 feet of ascent. It is measured by an instrument called the barometer.

BAROMETER

By definition, a barometer is an instrument for measuring the pressure of the atmosphere, as shown in Fig. 7-5. The instrument

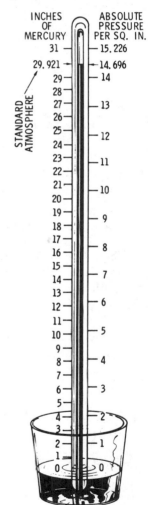

Fig. 7-5. A barometer illustrating the relationship between inches of mercury and absolute pressure in lbs. per sq. in.

159

consists of a glass tube 33 to 34 in. high, sealed at the top, filled with pure mercury, and inverted in an open cup of mercury. A graduated scale on the instrument permits observations of the fluctuations in the height of the mercury column. It is highest when the atmosphere is dry, weighing more then than when saturated with aqueous vapor, which is lighter than air. The height of barometric measurement is about 30 in.

The column of mercury remains suspended at this height because the weight of a column of mercury 30 in. high is the same as the weight of a like column of air about 50 miles high.

PRESSURE SCALES

The term *vacuum*, strictly speaking, is defined as a *space devoid of matter*. This is equivalent to saying *a space in which the pressure is zero*. According to common usage, it means *any space in which the pressure is less than that of the atmosphere*.

This gives rise to two scales of pressure:

1. Gauge.
2. Absolute.

When the hand of a steam gauge is at zero, the pressure actually existing is 14.74 lbs. (referred to a 30-in. barometer), or that of the atmosphere. The scale in the gauge is not marked at this point (14.74 lbs)., but at zero because, in the steam boiler as well as any other vessel under pressure, the important measurement is the difference of pressure between the inside and outside. This difference of pressure, or the effective pressure for doing work, is called the *gauge pressure* because it is measured by the gauge on the boiler.

The second pressure scale is known as *absolute pressure* because it gives the actual *pressure above zero*. In all calculations relative to the expansion of steam, the absolute pressure scale must be used. Gauge pressure is expressed as absolute pressure by adding 14.74, or for ordinary calculations, 14.7 lbs. Thus, 80 lbs. gauge pressure = 80 + 14.74 = 94.74 lbs. absolute pressure. Absolute pressure is expressed as gauge pressure by subtracting

14.7. Thus 90 lbs. absolute pressure = 90 − 14.7 = 75.3 lbs. gauge pressure.

The pressures below atmospheric pressure are usually expressed in lbs. per sq. in. when making calculations, or "inches of mercury" in practice. Thus, in the engine room, the expression "28 inches of vacuum" would signify an absolute pressure in the condenser of .946 lb. per sq. in. absolute. In other words, the mercury in a mercury column connected to a condenser having a 28-in. vacuum would rise to a height of 28 in., representing the difference between the pressure of the atmosphere and the pressure in the condenser, of 14.73 − .946 = 13.784 lbs. referred to a 30-in. barometer.

Pressure in lbs. per sq. in. is obtained by multiplying the barometer reading by .49116. Thus, a 30-in. barometer reading signifies a pressure of .49116 × 30 = 14.74 lbs. per sq. in.

Table 7-1 gives the pressure of the atmosphere in pounds per square inch for various readings of the barometer.

Rule—Barometer in inches of mercury × .49116 = lbs. per sq. in.

Table 7-1 is based on the standard atmosphere which, by definition, equals 29.921 in. of mercury, which equals 14.696 lbs. per sq. in., or 1 in. of mercury = 14.696 ÷ 29.921 = .49116 lbs. per sq. in.

THERMOMETERS

This term is generally applied to a glass tube terminating in a bulb charged with a liquid, usually mercury or colored alcohol. The liquid contracts or expands with changes of temperature, falling or rising in the tube against which is placed a graduated scale. The common scale is Fahrenheit, on which zero is the temperature of a mixture of salt and snow, 32° that of melting ice, and 212° that of boiling water. The Celsius and Reaumur scales, from the temperature of melting ice to that of boiling water, have 100 graduations and 80 graduations respectively. The Celsius is usually called the Centigrade thermometer. The latent heat varies with the boiling point—it decreases as the pressure rises.

161

Table 7-1. Atmospheric Pressure per Square Inch

Barometer (ins. of mercury)	Pressure (lbs. per sq. in.)	Barometer (ins. of mercury)	Pressure (lbs. per sq. in.)
28.00	13.75	29.291	14.696
28.25	13.88	30.00	14.74
28.50	14.00	30.25	14.86
28.75	14.12	30.50	14.98
29.00	14.24	30.75	15.10
29.25	14.37	31.00	15.23
29.50	14.49		
29.75	14.61		

STEAM

By definition, *steam is the hot invisible vapor given off by water at its boiling point.* The visible white vapor popularly known as steam is not steam but a collection of fine watery particles formed by the condensation of steam.

Steam is said to be:

1. *Saturated* when its temperature corresponds to its pressure.
2. *Superheated* when its temperature is above that due to its pressure.
3. *Gaseous steam* or *steam gas* when it is highly superheated.
4. *Dry* when it contains no moisture. It may be either saturated or superheated.
5. *Wet* when it contains intermingled mist or spray, its temperature corresponding to its pressure.

Steam exists when there is the proper relation between the temperature of the water and the external pressure. For instance, for a given temperature of the water, there is a certain external pressure above which steam will not form. Steam is produced by heating water until it reaches the *boiling point.* The latent heat of steam is the amount of heat required to change one pound of water into steam at the same temperature.

Thus, if heat is applied to a pound of pure water having a temperature of 212° F, steam will be formed and in a short time all of the water will be evaporated. If the temperature of the steam so formed is taken, the thermometer will register the same as the boiling water, which is 212°. It has been accurately determined by experiment that 970.4° of heat, or heat units, must be applied to a pound of boiling water to change it into steam at the same temperature, and this heat is called the latent heat of steam.

The various states of steam can be seen in the operation of a safety valve by closely observing it when blowing off pressure. For instance, when the safety valve of a boiler furnishing superheated steam blows off, a very interesting phenomenon can be observed. Very close to the valve the escaping gas is entirely invisible, being superheated at this point. Farther away, the outline of the ascending column is seen, the interior being invisible and gradually becoming "foggy." As the vapor ascends, it gradually reduces in temperature, and the steam becomes saturated and supersaturated, or wet, reaching the white state a little farther away where it is popularly and erroneously known as "steam." Steam is invisible. The reason the so-called wet steam can be seen is because wet steam is a mechanical mixture made up of saturated steam (which is invisible), which holds in suspension a multiplicity of fine water globules formed by condensation. It is the collection of water globules or condensate that is visible.

MECHANICAL POWERS

By definition, the mechanical powers are *mechanical contrivances that enter into the composition or formation of all machines.* They are:

1. The lever.
2. The wheel and axle.
3. The pulley.
4. The inclined plane.
5. The screw.
6. The wedge.

These can, in turn, be reduced to three classes:

1. A solid body turned on an axis.
2. A flexible cord.
3. A hard and smooth inclined surface.

The mechanism of the wheel and axle, and of the pulley, merely

163

combines the principle of *the lever* with the tension of the cords. The properties of the screw depend entirely upon those of the lever and the inclined plane; and the case of the wedge is analogous to that of a body sustained between two inclined planes. They all depend for their action upon what is known as the *principle of work*, one of the important principles in mechanics and in the study of machine elements.

The principle of work states that, neglecting frictional or other losses, *the applied force multiplied by the distance through which it moves equals the resistance overcome multiplied by the distance through which it is overcome.* A force acting through a given distance can be made to overcome a greater force acting as a resistance through a shorter distance. No possible arrangement can be made to overcome a greater force through the same distance. The principle of work may be also stated as follows:

Work put into a machine = lost work + work done
by the machine

The principle holds true in every case. It applies equally to a simple lever, the most complex mechanism, or to a so-called *perpetual motion* machine. No machine can be made to perform work unless a somewhat greater amount (enough to make up for the losses) is applied by some external agent. In a perpetual motion machine, no such outside force is supposed to be applied; it is therefore against the laws of mechanics.

THE LEVER

The lever consists of an inflexible bar or rod, which is supported at some point, and is freely movable about that point as a center of motion. In the lever, three points are to be considered; the *fulcrum* or point about which the lever turns, the point where the *force* is applied, and the point where the *weight* is applied. There are three varieties of the lever, as shown in Fig. 7-6. They differ according to where the *fulcrum*, the *weight*, or the *power* is respectively placed between the other two, but the action in every case is reducible to the same principle and the same general rule applies to them all.

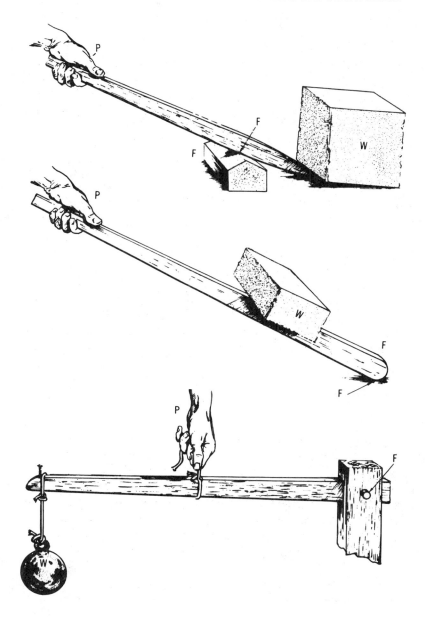

Fig. 7-6. Three kinds of levers.

The following general rule holds for all classes of levers:

Rule—The force P, multiplied by its distance from the *fulcrum*, is equal to the load W multiplied by its distance from the fulcrum. That is:

$$\text{Force} \times \text{distance} = \text{load} \times \text{distance}$$

Example—What force applied at 3 ft. from the fulcrum will balance a weight of 112 lbs. applied at a distance of 6 in. from the fulcrum?

Here, the distances or leverages are 3 ft. and 6 in. The distance must be of the same denomination; hence, reducing ft. to in., $3 \times 12 = 36$ in.

Applying the rule:

$$\text{Force} \times 36 = 112 \times 6$$

$$\text{Force} = \frac{112 \times 6}{36} = 18.67 \text{ or } 18\tfrac{2}{3} \text{ lbs.}$$

This solution holds for all levers illustrated in Fig. 7-7.

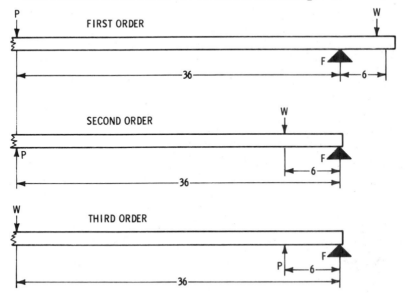

Fig. 7-7. The three orders of levers.

THE WHEEL AND AXLE

This combination is virtually a continuous or revolving lever. It consists of a wheel fixed to an axle or drum so arranged that the operating force is applied to the wheel and the load to the axle, as shown in Fig. 7-8. Comparison of the wheel and axle with a first-order lever shows that, in principle, they are the same.

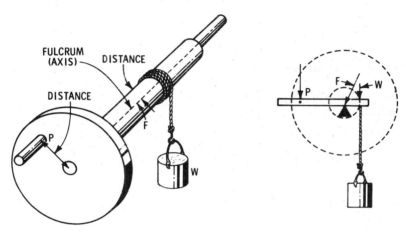

Fig. 7-8. A wheel and axle compared to a lever.

CHINESE WHEEL AND AXLE

This is a modification of the wheel and axle, and is used for obtaining extreme degrees of leverage. Its principle and construction are shown in Fig. 7-9.

THE PULLEY

In its simplest form a pulley consists of a grooved wheel, called a sheave, turning within a frame by means of a cord or rope. It works in contact with the groove in order to transmit the force applied to the rope in another direction, as shown in Fig. 7-10. Pulleys are divided into *fixed* and *movable*. In the fixed pulley, no mechanical advantage is gained, but its use is of the greatest

167

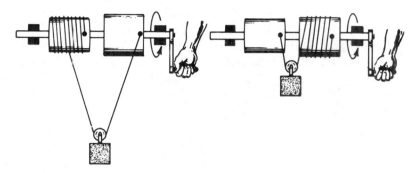

Fig. 7-9. Chinese windlass hoist.

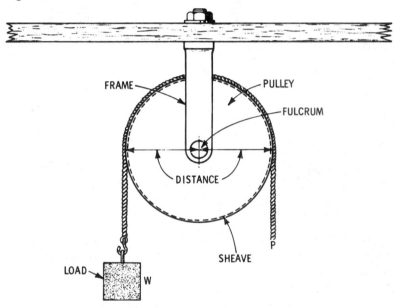

Fig. 7-10. A simple pulley.

importance in accomplishing the work appropriate to the pulley, such as raising water from a well. The *movable* pulley, by distributing the weights into separate parts, is attended by mechanical advantages proportional to the number of points of support.

Combinations of pulleys are arranged with several sheaves in one frame to form a *block* to increase the load that may be lifted per unit of force applied; in other words, to increase the leverage.

168

All such arrangements are virtually equivalents of the lever. The following rule expresses the relation between the force and load.

Rule—The load capable of being lifted by a combination of pulleys is equal to the force × the number of ropes supporting the lower or movable block.

THE INCLINED PLANE

This mechanical power consists of an inclined flat surface upon which a weight may be raised, as shown in Fig. 7-11. By such substitution of a sloping path for a direct upward line of ascent, a given weight can be raised by another weight weighing less than the weight to be raised. The inclined plane becomes a mechanical

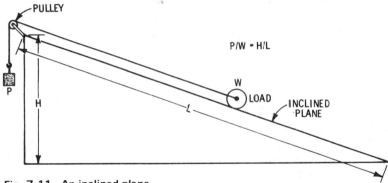

Fig. 7-11. An inclined plane.

power in consequence of its supporting part of the weight, and leaving only a part to be supported by the power. Thus, the power has to encounter only a portion of the force of gravity at a time; a portion which is more or less according to how much the plane is elevated. The following rule expresses these relations:

Rule—As the applied force P is to the load W, so is the height H to the length of the plane W. That is:

$$\text{Force} : \text{load} = \text{height} : \text{plane length}$$

Example—What force (P) is necessary to raise a load of 10 lbs. if the height is 2 ft. and the plane is 12 ft.?

169

Substituting in the equation:

$$P : 10 = 2 : 12$$
$$P \times 12 = 2 \times 10$$
$$P = \frac{10 \times 2}{12} = \frac{20}{12} = 1\,\tfrac{2}{3} \text{ lbs.}$$

THE SCREW

This is simply an inclined plane wrapped around a cylinder. The evolution of a screw from an inclined plane is shown in Fig. 7-12. The distance between two consecutive coils, measured from center to center or from upper side to upper side (literally the height of the inclined plane for one revolution), is the *pitch* of the screw.

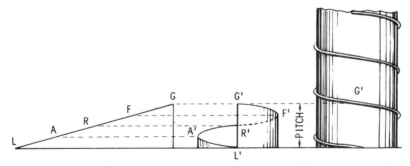

Fig. 7-12. Evolution of a screw.

The screw is generally employed when severe pressure is to be exerted through small distances. A screw in one revolution will descend a distance equal to its pitch, or the distance between two threads. The force applied to the screw will move through (in the same time) the circumference of a circle whose diameter is twice the length of the lever.

Rule—As the applied force is to the load, so is the pitch to the length of the thread per turn. That is:

Applied force : load = pitch : length of thread per turn

Example—If the distance between the threads or pitch is ¼ in.

and a force of 100 lbs. is applied at the circumference of the screw, what weight will be moved by the screw, if the length of the thread per turn of the screw is 10 in.?

Substituting in the equation:

$$100 : \text{load} = \frac{1}{4} : 10$$

$$\text{load} \times \frac{1}{4} = 10 \times 100$$

$$\text{load} = \frac{10 \times 100}{\frac{1}{4}} = 4000 \text{ lbs.}$$

THE WEDGE

This is virtually a pair of inclined planes in contact along their bases, or back to back. The wedge is generally driven by blows of a hammer or sledge instead of being pushed, as in the case of the other powers, although the wedge is sometimes moved by constant pressure. If the weight rests on a horizontal plane and a wedge is forced under it, the weight will be lifted a height equal to the thickness of the butt end of the wedge when the wedge has penetrated its length, as in Fig. 7-13.

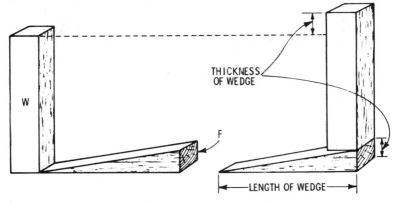

THICKNESS OF WEDGE

W

F

LENGTH OF WEDGE

Fig. 7-13. The application of the wedge in raising a heavy load.

Rule—As the applied force is to the load, so is the thickness of the wedge to its length. That is:

171

Applied force : load = thickness : length of wedge

Example—What force is necessary to apply to a wedge 20 in. long and 4 in. thick to raise a load of 2000 lbs.?
Substituting in the equation:

Applied force : 2000 = 4 : 20

20 : 4 = 2000 : applied force

applied force × 20 = 4 × 2000

$$\text{applied force} = \frac{4 \times 2000}{20} = 400 \, \text{lbs.}$$

EXPANSION AND CONTRACTION

Practically all substances expand with an increase in temperature and contract with a decrease in temperature. The expansion of solid bodies in a longitudinal direction is known as *linear expansion;* the expansion in volume is called the *volumetric expansion.* A noticeable exception to the general law for expansion is the behavior of water. With a decrease in temperature, water will contract until it reaches its minimum volume, at a temperature of 39.1° F. This is the point of maximum density. With a continued decrease in temperature, the water will expand until it freezes and becomes ice, as shown in Fig. 7-14. Were it not for this fact, plumbers would be out of the job of repairing frozen pipes.
The following example will illustrate the use of Table 7-2.

Example—How much longer is a 36-in. rod of aluminum when heated from 97° to 200° F?

Increase in temperature is 200 − 97 = 103°

Coefficient of expansion for aluminum
from Table 7-2 = .00001234

Increase in length of rod =
36 × .00001234 × 103 = .0456 in.

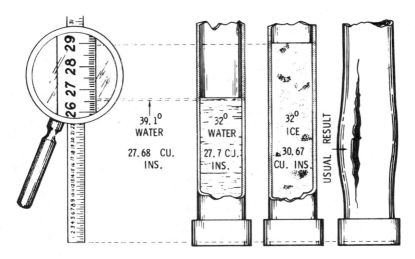

Fig. 7-14. The expansion of water at various temperatures.

Table 7-2. Linear Expansion of Common Metals (32°-212°F)

Metal	Linear expansion per unit length per degree F	Metal	Linear expansion per unit length per degree F
Aluminum	.00001234	Iron, wrought	.00000648
Antimony	.00000627	Lead	.00001571
Bismuth	.00000975	Nickel	.00000695
Brass	.00000957	Steel	.00000636
Bronze	.00000986	Tin	.00001163
Copper	.00000887	Zinc, cast }	.00001407
Gold	.00000786	Zinc, rolled }	
Iron, cast	.00000556		

Volumetric expansion = 3 × linear expansion.

MELTING POINT OF SOLIDS

The temperatures at which a solid substance changes into a liquid is called the melting point. When a solid begins to melt, the temperature remains constant until the whole mass of the solid has changed into a liquid. The heat supplied during the period is used to change the substance from the solid to the liquid state and is called the *latent heat of fusion.*

173

For instance, to melt a pound of ice at 32° F requires 143.57 Btu, or 144 Btu for ordinary calculations. The temperature at which melting takes place varies for different substances, as shown in Table 7-3.

Impure metals usually have a lower melting point than pure metals. Low melting points may be obtained by combining several metals to form alloys. Often an alloy will melt at a much lower temperature than would be expected, considering the melting points of the metals of which it is composed. Those of the lowest melting point contain bismuth, lead, tin, and cadmium.

By varying the percentages of each metal, melting points ranging from 149° to 324° F are obtained; these are only about one-fourth the melting point of the constituent metals. Alloys having such low fusing points are known as *low-fusing alloys*. These are considered further in the chapters on Soldering and Lead work.

Table 7-3. Melting Points of Commercial Metals

Metal	Degrees F
Aluminum	1,200
Antimony	1,150
Bismuth	500
Brass	1,700 -1,850
Copper	1,940
Cadmium	610
Iron, cast	2,300
Iron, wrought	2,900
Lead	620
Mercury	−38
Steel	2,500
Tin	446
Zinc, cast	785

GRAVITY

By definition, gravity is *the force that attracts bodies, at or near the surface of the earth, toward the center of the earth.* This force varies at different points on the earth's surface. It is strongest at sea level, decreasing below sea level in the same ratio that its distance from the center of the earth decreases. Above the surface, the attraction decreases in ratio as the square of the distance from the center of the earth increases. Thus, a body weighs less on top of a high mountain than at sea level.

Falling Bodies

Under the influence of gravity *alone* all bodies fall to the earth with the same acceleration of velocity. Galileo proved this by dropping balls of different sizes at the same instant from the top of the leaning tower of Pisa. The spectators saw the balls start together and heard them strike the ground together. Of course, anybody knows that if, for instance, a feather and a piece of lead were released at the same time from an elevated point, the lead would reach the ground first. It is not the difference in weight that retards the feather but the effect of the air on the less dense object. In a vacuum, all bodies fall with the same acceleration of velocity, as has been proved by the experiment illustrated in Fig. 7-15.

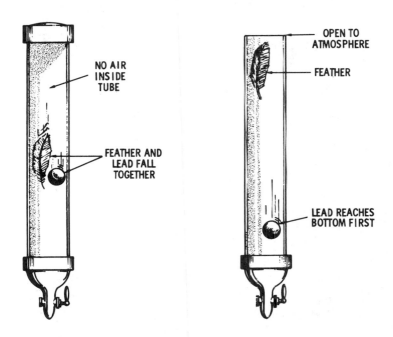

Fig. 7-15. Experiment with falling bodies.

Center of Gravity

Briefly, the center of gravity of a body is *that point of the body about which all its parts are balanced, or which being supported, the whole body will remain at rest though acted upon by gravity.* The center of gravity may be found by calculation and, in some cases, more conveniently by experiments, as in Fig. 7-16.

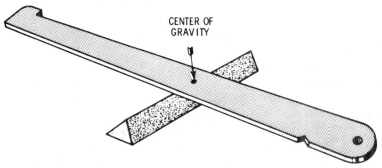

CENTER OF
GRAVITY

Fig. 7-16. Method of finding the center of gravity.

Momentum

In popular language, momentum may be defined as *the power of overcoming resistance as possessed by a body by virtue of its motion;* that which makes a moving body hard to stop. Numerically, it is equal to the product of the mass of the body multiplied by its velocity. It is numerically equivalent to the number of pounds of force that will stop a moving body in 1 second, or the number of pounds of force which, acting during 1 second, will give it the given velocity.

Friction

By definition, friction is *that force which acts between two bodies at their surface of contact so as to resist their sliding on each other;* it is the resistance to motion when one body is moved upon another. Were it not for friction, many things would be impossible in mechanics. For instance, power could not be transmitted by belts, and automobiles could not be driven through clutches.

Because of friction, bearings must be lubricated, long pipe lines must be oversize to prevent undue loss of pressure, etc. The object of lubricating bearings is to form a film of oil so that the revolving part does not touch the bearing but revolves on the oil; the friction of solids on fluids is much less than that between solids. Ordinary bearings absorb from 3% to 5% of the applied power; roller bearings, 2%; ball bearings, 1%; spur gears with cast teeth, including bearings, 7%; spur gears with cut teeth, 4%; bevel gears with cast teeth, including bearings, 8%; bevel gears with cut teeth, including bearings, 5%; belting, 2% to 4%; roller chains, 3% to 5%.

HYDRAULICS

The term *hydraulics* is commonly, though ill-advisedly, defined as *the science that treats of liquids, especially water, in motion.* Properly speaking, there are two general divisions of the subject:

1. Hydrostatics.
2. Hydrodynamics.

Hydrostatics refers to liquids *at rest,* and hydrodynamics to liquids *in motion.* The outline given relates to water.

Water

Those who have had experience in the design or operation of pumps have found that water is an unyielding substance when confined in pipes and pump passages. This necessitates very substantial construction to withstand the pressure and periodic shocks or water hammer. Water at its maximum density (39.1° F) will expand as heat is added, and it will also expand slightly as the temperature falls from this point.

For ordinary calculations, the weight of 1 cu. ft. of water is taken at 62.4 lbs., which is correct when its temperature is 53° F. At 62° F the weight is 62.355 lbs. The weight of a U.S. gallon of water, or 231 cu. in., is roughly 8⅓ lbs.

Head and Pressure

These are the two primary considerations in hydraulics. The word *head* signifies *the difference in level of water between two points,* and is usually expressed in feet. Two kinds of head are:

1. Static.
2. Dynamic.

The *static head* is the height from a given point of a column or body of water at rest, considered as causing or measuring pressure. The *dynamic head* is an equivalent or virtual head of water in motion which represents the resulting pressure due to the height of the water from a given point, and the resistance to flow due to friction. Thus, when water is made to flow through pipes or nozzles, there is a loss of head. In ordinary calculations, it is common practice to estimate that every foot of head is equal to one-half pound pressure per sq. in., as this allows for ordinary friction in pipes.

The following distinctions with reference to head should be carefully noted.

Total static head = static lift + static head.
Total dynamic head = dynamic lift + dynamic head.

Lift

When the barometer reads 30 in. at sea level, the pressure of the atmosphere at that elevation is 14.74 lbs. per sq. in. This pressure will maintain or balance a column of water 34.042 ft. high when the column is completely exhausted of air, and the water is at a temperature of 62° F. The pressure of the atmosphere then *lifts* the water to such a height as will establish equilibrium between the weight of the water and the pressure of the air. Similarly, in pump operation, the receding piston or plunger establishes the vacuum and the pressure of the atmosphere lifts the water from the level of the supply to the level of the pump. Accordingly, lift as related to pump operation may be defined as *the height in feet from the surface of the intake supply to the pump.*

Strictly speaking, lift is the height to which the water is elevated by atmospheric pressure, which in some pumps may be measured by the elevation of the inlet valve and in others by the elevation of the piston. The practical limit of lift is 20 to 25 ft. Long inlet lines, many inlet elbows, and high temperature of the water require shorter lifts. The lift must be reduced as the temperature of the water is increased, because the boiling point of water corresponds to the pressure.

Theoretically, a perfect pump will draw water from a height of 34 ft. when the barometer reads 30 in., but since a perfect vacuum cannot be obtained due to valve leakage, air entrained in the water, and the vapor of the water itself, the actual height is generally less than 30 ft., and for warm or hot water, considerably less. When the water is warm the height to which it can be lifted decreases due to the increased pressure of the vapor. For example, a boiler feed pump taking water at 153° F could not produce a vacuum greater than 20.78 in. because, at that point, the water would begin to boil and fill the pump chamber with steam. Accordingly, the theoretical lift corresponding would be:

$$34 \times \frac{21.78}{30} = 24.68 \text{ ft., approximately}$$

The result is approximate because no correction has been made for the 34 which represents a 34-ft. column of water at 62°; of course, at 153° the length of such a column would be slightly increased. It should be noted that the figure 24.68 ft. is *approximate* theoretical lift for water at 153°; the *practical* lift would be considerably less. Table 7-4 shows the theoretical maximum lift for different temperatures, leakage not considered.

Table 7-4. Theoretical Lift for Various Temperatures

Temp. F	Absolute pressure of vapor lbs. per sq. in.	Vacuum in inches of mercury	Lift in feet	Temp. F	Absolute pressure of vapor lbs. per sq. in.	Vacuum in inches of mercury	Lift in feet
102.1	1	27.88	31.6	182.9	8	13.63	15.4
126.3	2	25.85	29.3	188.3	9	11.6	13.0
141.6	3	23.83	27	193.2	10	9.56	10.8
153.1	4	21.78	24.7	197.8	11	7.52	8.5
162.3	5	19.74	22.3	202	12	5.49	6.2
170.1	6	17.70	20	205.9	13	3.45	3.9
176.9	7	15.67	17.7	209.6	14	1.41	1.6

FLOW OF WATER IN PIPES

The quantity of water discharged through a pipe depends on:

1. The *head*, which is the vertical distance between the level

179

surface of still water in the chamber at the entrance end of the pipe and the level of the center of the discharge end of the pipe.

2. The length of the pipe.

3. The smoothness of the interior surface of the pipe.

4. The number and sharpness of the bends. But it is independent of the position of the pipe, as horizontal or inclined upward or downward. The head, instead of being an actual distance between levels, may be caused by pressure, as a pump, in which case the head is calculated as a vertical distance corresponding to the pressure. 1 lb. per sq. in. = 2.309 ft. head, or 1 ft. head = .433 lb. per sq. in.

ELEMENTARY PUMPS

There are three elements necessary for the operation of a pump:

1. Inlet or suction valve.
2. Piston or plunger.
3. Discharge valve.

Simple pumps may be divided into two classes:

1. Lift pumps.
2. Force pumps.

A lift pump is one which does not elevate the water higher than the lift; a force pump operates against both lift and head.

Lift Pumps

Fig. 7-17 shows the essentials and working principle of a simple lift pump. In this type of pump there are two valves which are known as the *foot valve* and the *bucket valve*. During the up stroke, the bucket valve is closed and the foot valve is open, allowing the atmosphere to force the water into the cylinder. When the piston begins to descend, the foot valve closes and the bucket valve opens, which transfers the water in the cylinder from the lower side of the piston to the upper side.

During the next up stroke, the water already transferred to the upper side of the piston is discharged through the outlet. It will be noted that as the piston begins the up stroke of discharge it is

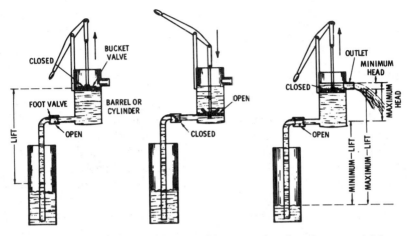

Fig. 7-17. Elementary single-acting lift pump showing the essential features and cycle of operation.

subject to a small maximum head, and at the end of the up stroke to a minimum head. This variable head is so small in comparison to the head against which a force pump works that it is not ordinarily considered.

Force Pumps

The essential feature of a force pump, which distinguishes it from a lift pump, is that *the cylinder is always closed;* in a lift pump it is *alternately closed and open* when the piston is respectively at the upper and lower ends of its stroke. In addition to the foot and bucket valves of the lift pump, a head valve is provided.

In operation, during the up stroke, atmospheric pressure forces water into the cylinder, and during the down stroke this water is transferred from the lower to the upper side of the piston. During the next up stroke the piston forces the water out of the cylinder through the head valve, which closes when the piston reaches the end of the stroke and the cycle is repeated.

A simple form of force pump is one known as a single-acting plunger pump. In operation, during the up stroke, water fills the cylinder, the inlet valve opens, and the outlet valve closes. During the down stroke, the plunger displaces the water in the barrel, forcing it through the discharge valve against the pressure head.

181

A piston is *shorter* than the stroke, whereas a plunger is *longer* than the stroke. The word plunger is very frequently used erroneously for a piston.

Double-Acting Force Pump

By fitting a set of inlet and outlet valves at each end of a pump cylinder, it is made double-acting; that is, a cylinder full of water is pumped each stroke instead of every other stroke. With this arrangement, the piston can have approximately half the area of the single-acting piston for equal displacement. Accordingly, the maximum stresses brought on the reciprocating parts are reduced approximately one-half, thus permitting lighter and more compact construction. In the double-acting pump there are no bucket valves, a solid piston being used. The essential features and operation are plainly shown in Fig. 7-18. There are two inlet valves, A and B, and two discharge valves, C and D, the cylinder being closed and provided with a piston. In operation, during the down stroke, water follows the upper face of the piston through valve A. At the same time, the previous charge is forced out of the cylinder

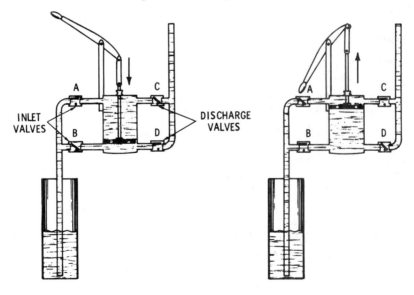

Fig. 7-18. Elementary double-acting force pump.

through valve D by the lower face of the piston. During these simultaneous operations, valves A and D remain open, and B and C are closed.

During the up stroke, water follows the lower face of the piston through valve B. At the same time, the previous charge is forced out of the cylinder through valve C by the upper face of the piston. During these simultaneous operations, valves B and C remain open, and A and D are closed.

CHAPTER 8

General Plumbing Information

The ability to perform basic calculations is a prime necessity, not only to get a plumber's license, but for the master plumber as well. With this in mind, a number of practical examples, or problems bearing on the subject matter, have been calculated. Although requirements for a plumber's license differ in various localities, the problems given are of a type usually found in license examinations for master plumbers. In this connection, it should be impressed upon all candidates for licenses the great necessity of study to master the fundamental principles underlying each example given, in order to increase abilities and be able to solve any new or similar problem at the written examination.

Example—A water tank is 65 in. long and has a trapezoidal cross section. The two parallel sides are 32 in. and 44 in., and the distance between them is 40 in. Determine the capacity of the tank in gallons.

Solution—The formula for calculating the area of a trapezoid is:

$$A = \frac{1}{2} H (a + b)$$

where

H is the distance between the two parallel sides
a and b is the length of the parallel sides
A is the area

A substitution of numerical values gives:

$$A = \frac{1}{2} \times 40\,(32 + 44) = 1520 \text{ sq. in.}$$

The volume in cubic inches $= 1520 \times 65 = 98,800$

Since there are 231 cubic inches in one gallon, the gallon contents of the tank =

$$\frac{98,800}{231} = 427.7 \text{ gals.}$$

Example—What is the radius of a circle the area of which is equal to that of a rectangle whose sides are 26.9 and 12.5 in. respectively?

Solution—Area of rectangle $= 26.9 \times 12.5 = 336.25$ sq. in.

Area of circle $= \pi R^2 = 336.25$ sq. in.

From which $R = \sqrt{\dfrac{336.25}{\pi}} = 10.34$ in.

Example—What is the weight of a solid ball of brass 6 inches in diameter? Assume specific gravity $= 8.4$.

Solution—The cubic contents of the ball is obtained by the use of the following formula:

$$V = \frac{4\pi R^2}{3} = \frac{4\pi \times 3^3}{3} = 113.1 \text{ cu. in.}$$

Weight of the ball equals the weight of one cubic inch of water × specific gravity of brass × circumference of the ball. Therefore:

Weight of ball $= 0.0361 \times 8.4 \times 113.1 = 34.3$ lbs.

186

Example—Find the height of a cast-iron cone whose weight is 533.4 kilograms, and whose diameter at the base is 5 decimeters. (Specific gravity of cast iron = 7.22.)

Solution—The cubic content of the cone is:

$$\frac{533.4}{7.22} = 73.9 \text{ cubic decimeters}$$

$$\text{Volume of cone} = \frac{\text{base area} \times H}{3}$$

It follows that

$$73.9 = \frac{5 \times 5 \times 0.7854 \times H}{3}$$

and

$$H = \frac{3 \times 73.9}{5 \times 5 \times 0.7854}$$

$$= 11.3 \text{ decimeters, or } 11.3 \times 3.937$$
$$= 44.5 \text{ inches (approx.)}$$

Example—In a certain plumbing installation, three pipes have an internal diameter of 2, 2½, and 3 inches, respectively. What is the diameter of a pipe having an area equal to the three pipes?

Solution—The areas of the three pipes are as follows:

$$A_1 + A_2 + A_3 \times \frac{\pi \times 2^2}{4} + \frac{\pi \times 2.5^2}{4} + \frac{\pi \times 3^2}{4} =$$

$$\frac{\pi}{4} (2^2 + 2.5^2 + 3^2) = \frac{\pi}{4} (4 + 6.25 + 9) = \frac{\pi}{4} \times 19.25 \text{ sq. in.}$$

Since the formula for a circular area is $\dfrac{\pi \times D^2}{4}$ we obtain,

$$\frac{\pi}{4} \times 19.25 = \frac{\pi}{4} \times D^2, \text{ or } D^2 = 19.25 \text{ sq. in.}$$

Therefore,

$$D = \sqrt{19.25}, \text{ or } 4.39 \text{ inches.}$$

187

Remember that the area of any circular pipe is directly proportional to the square of its diameter in inches, so our calculation will be somewhat simplified. We have:

$$2^2 + 2.5^2 + 3^2 = D^2$$

or,

$$D = \sqrt{19.25} = 4.39 \text{ inches}$$

It follows from the foregoing that the area of a pipe having the same capacity as a 2-, 2½-, and 3-in.-diameter pipe together, must be 4.39 in. in diameter, or $4\,^{25}\!/_{64}$ in.

Example—If a 1-in. pipe delivers 10 gal. of water per minute, what size of pipe will be required to deliver 20 gal. per minute?

Solution—In this problem, it is necessary to find the diameter of a piece of pipe whose area is twice as large as one that is 1 inch in diameter.

Since the area for any circular section $= \dfrac{\pi D^2}{4}$, it follows that the area for the 1-in. pipe is $\dfrac{\pi \times 1^2}{4} = 0.7854$ sq. in. A pipe having twice this area consequently has a diameter of $\dfrac{\pi}{2}$. Thus, $\dfrac{\pi}{2} = \dfrac{\pi D^2}{4}$, which after rearrangement of terms gives $D^2 = 2$, or $D = \sqrt{2} = 1.4142$ inches. That is, the required diameter of a pipe to deliver 20 gpm is $1\,^{13}\!/_{32}$ inches (approximately).

Example—If the total fall of a house sewer is 24 in. per 120 ft., what is the slope per foot of this sewer?

Solution—Since the sewer has a total length of 120 ft., the slope per foot is $^{24}\!/_{120}$, or 0.2 in.

Example—What is the weight of 1 cu. in. of water if it is assumed that 1 cu. ft. weighs 62.5 lbs.?

Solution—1 cu. ft. contains 12 × 12 × 12, or 1728 cu. in. Therefore, 1 cu. in. weighs $^{62.5}\!/_{1728}$, or 0.0361 lb. This figure is given in

188

most handbooks and is frequently used to calculate water pressure in tanks, pipes, etc.

Example—What is the weight of a column of water 12 in. high and 1 in. in diameter?

Solution—Since 1 cu. in. of water weighs 0.0361 lb., a column of water 12 in. high weighs 12 × 0.0361, or 0.4332 lb.

Example—What is the pressure in pounds per square inch (psi) at the base of a 10-ft. water cylinder?

Solution—The pressure may be found by remembering that the 10-ft. water column weighs 10 × 12 × 0.0361, or 4.332 psi.

Example—Calculate the minimum water pressure at the city water main, in pounds per square inch (psi), necessary to fill a house tank located on top of a 6-story building when the inlet to the water tank is located at an elevation of 110 ft. above the city water main.

Solution—Since 1 cu. in. of water weighs 0.0361 lb., the minimum pressure required is 12 × 110 × 0.0361, or 47.7 psi.

Example—A water tank 10 ft. high and 15 ft. across is to be constructed of wood. When filled to the bottom of the overflow pipe, its capacity is 11,000 gals. How high above the inside bottom of the tank should the bottom of the overflow pipe be in order to have the required water capacity in the tank? (One cubic foot equals 7.48 gals.).

Solution—The area of the tank in square feet multiplied by the assumed height of the water in the tank in feet equals the cubic content of the water in cubic feet. Since 1 cu. ft. equals 7.48 gals., the cubic content occupied by the water is $11000/7.48$, or 1470.6 cu. ft.

The equation required for our calculation will therefore be as follows:

189

$$7.5^2 \times \pi \times H = 1470.6$$

$$H = \frac{1470.6}{56.25\pi} = 8.32\,\text{ft.}$$

Thus, the bottom of the overflow pipe should be located 8.32 ft. or 8 ft. 3 $^{27}/_{32}$ in. above the bottom of the tank.

Example—What is the number of horsepower required to raise 40,000 lbs. 200 ft. in 5 minutes? Disregard losses.

Solution—By definition, 1 horsepower is equivalent to doing work at a rate of 33,000 lbs. per minute. Thus, in the present problem

$$HP = \frac{\text{foot-pounds}}{33,000 \times t}$$

where

HP is the horsepower required
t is the time in minutes

Substituting values, we obtain

$$HP = \frac{\text{foot-pounds}}{33,000 \times t} = \frac{40,000 \times 200}{33,000 \times 5} = 48.5\,HP$$

Example—What is the number of horsepower required to lift 10,000 gals. of water per hour to a height of 90 ft.? Disregard losses. (Assume weight of water to be 8⅓ lbs. per gallon.)

Solution:

$$HP = \frac{\text{foot-pounds}}{33,000 \times t} = \frac{10,000 \times 8\frac{1}{3} \times 90}{33,000 \times 60} = 3.79\,HP$$

Example—A city of 25,000 uses 15 gals. of water per day per capita. If it is required to raise this water 150 ft., what is the number of horsepower required? Disregard losses.

190

Solution:

$$HP = \frac{\text{foot-pounds}}{33,000 \times t}$$

$$= \frac{15 \times 8\tfrac{1}{3} \times 25,000 \times 150}{33,000 \times 60 \times 24} = HP \text{ (approx.)}$$

Example—How many gallons of water can a 75-HP engine raise 150 ft. high in 5 hours? One gallon of water weighs 8⅓ lbs. Disregard losses.

Solution—If the given data is substituted in our formula for horsepower, we obtain:

$$75 = \frac{150 \times 8\tfrac{1}{3} \times G}{33,000 \times 5 \times 60}$$

$$G = \frac{75 \times 33,000 \times 5 \times 60}{150 \times 8\tfrac{1}{3}} = 594,000 \text{ gallons}$$

Example—A circular tank 20 ft. deep and 20 ft. in diameter is filled with water. If the average height to which the water is to be lifted is 50 ft., what must be the horsepower of an engine capable of pumping the water out in 2 hours? Disregard losses.

Solution—In this example, it is first necessary to calculate the cubic content of the tank; that is, the cross-sectional area multiplied by its height. Thus,

volume in cu. ft. $= \pi R^2 H = \pi \times 10^2 \times 20 + 6283$ cu ft.

Since 1 cu. ft. of water weighs 62.5 lbs., the total weight of the tank's contents is:

$$62.5 \times 6283 = 392,700 \text{ lbs. (approx.)}$$

Again, using our formula, we have:

$$HP = \frac{\text{foot-pounds}}{33,000 \times t} = \frac{392,700 \times 5}{33,000 \times 2 \times 60} = 5\,HP \text{ (approx.)}$$

Example—The suction lift on a pump is 10 ft. and the head pumped against is 100 ft. If the loss due to friction in the pipe line is assumed as 9 ft., and the pump delivers 100 gals. per minute, what is the horsepower delivered by the pump?

Solution—When the water delivered is expressed in gallons per minute (usually written gpm) the formula for horsepower is:

$$HP = \frac{gpm \times head\ in\ feet \times 8.33}{33,000}$$

A substitution of values gives

$$HP = \frac{100 \times 119 \times 8.33}{33,000} = 3\,HP$$

Example—A tank having a capacity of 10,000 gals. must be emptied in 2 hours. What capacity pump is required?

Solution—The capacity of the pump in gallons per minute (gpm) is arrived at by dividing the total gallonage of the tank by the time in minutes. Thus,

$$gpm = \frac{10,000}{2 \times 60} = 83.3\,gpm$$

Example—What is the net capacity of a double-acting pump having a piston diameter of 3 in. and a stroke of 5 in. when it makes 75 strokes per minute? Assume slip of pump = 5%.

Solution—The rule for obtaining pump capacity is as follows: *Multiply the area of the piston in square inches by the length of the stroke in inches, and by the number of delivery strokes per minute; divide the product by 231 to obtain the theoretical capacity in U.S. gallons.*

This rule is most commonly stated in a formula as follows:

$$gpm = \frac{D^2 \times 0.7854 \times L \times N}{231}$$

where,

gpm = number of gallons pumped per minute
D = diameter of plunger or piston in inches
L = length of stroke in inches
N = number of delivery strokes per minute

A substitution of values in the above formula gives:

$$gpm = \frac{3^2 \times 0.7854 \times 5 \times 75}{231} = 11.5$$

With a slip of 5%, the total net capacity of the pump is finally 11.5 × 0.95 = 10.9 gpm.

Example—What is the hourly net capacity of a 2 × 8 double-acting power pump running at 150 rpm and having a slip of 10%?

Solution—The formula for pump capacity is:

$$gpm = \frac{D^2 \times 0.7854 \times L \times N}{231}$$

$$= \frac{2^2 \times 0.7854 \times 8 \times 300}{231} = 32.7\,gpm$$

The hourly net capacity = 32.7 × 60 × 0.9 = 1765.8 gals.

It should be observed that if N is taken to represent the number of revolutions of a single double-acting pump, the result is to be multiplied by 2, and if N represents the number of revolutions of a duplex pump, which would be the same as two single pumps, the result must be multiplied by 4.

Example—What is the capacity of a double-acting pump in gallons per minute if the cylinder is 9 in. in diameter, and the stroke 10 in., when it makes 60 strokes per minute? (Disregard slippage.)

Solution—The capacity of the pump in gallons per minute (gpm) is

$$gpm = \frac{D^2 \times 0.8754 \times L \times N}{231}$$

$$= \frac{9^2 \times 0.7854 \times 10 \times 60}{231}$$

$$= 165.2\,gpm$$

Example—A gas engine has a 4-in. piston and the effective pressure acting upon it is 50 lbs. per sq. in. What is the total load on the piston?

Solution—In this example, it is first necessary to determine the total net area of the piston. In multiplying this area by the pressure, we obtain the total load acting upon the piston. Thus,

$$A = \frac{\pi \times 4^2}{4} = 12.57 \text{ sq. in.}$$

$$\text{Total load} = 12.57 \times 50 = 628.5 \text{ lbs.}$$

Example—What is the indicated horsepower of a 4-cylinder 5 × 6 engine running at 500 rpm and 50 lbs. per sq. in. effective pressure?

Solution—The well-known formula for calculation of indicated horsepower is:

$$\text{IHP} = \frac{\text{PLAN}}{33,000} \times K$$

where coefficient (K) = 2 (four-cylinder engine). Substituting our values, we obtain:

$$\text{IHP} = \frac{50 \times 6/12 \times 0.7854 \times 5^2 \times 500}{33,000} \times 2 = 14.87$$

Example—The temperature of a furnace as registered by a pyrometer is 2750° F. What is the corresponding reading in Centigrade degrees?

Solution—The equation is:

$$C = \tfrac{5}{9} (F - 32)$$

$$C = \tfrac{5}{9} (2750 - 32) = 1510°$$

Example—A pail contains 58 lbs. of water having a temperature of 40° F. If heat is applied until the temperature of the water reaches 95° F, what is the amount of Btu supplied to the water?

Solution—The rise in temperature has been 95 − 40 = 55° F. Since one Btu is one pound raised one degree, it follows that to raise 58 pounds 55 degrees requires:

194

58 × 55 = 3190 Btu

Example—How many heat units (Btu) are required to raise one pound of water from 55° to 212° F? How many units of work does this represent?

Solution—The number of heat units required is 1 (212 − 55) = 157 Btu.

Since the mechanical equivalent of heat is 778, it is only necessary to multiply the number of heat units by this constant to obtain the equivalent number of work units. Thus,

157 × 778 = 122,146 foot-pounds

Example—In a certain pump installation, it was found that a 2-in. pipe, due to corrosion, had an effective diameter of only 1½ in. Calculate the loss in cross-sectional area due to corrosion.

Solution—It may easily be shown that the area of any circular pipe varies as the square of its diameter. The loss in cross-sectional area is therefore:

(2 × 2) − (1.5 × 1.5) = 4 − 2.25, or 1.75

1.75 × .7854 = 1.37 sq. in. loss

(Note: .7854 = area for a 1-in. pipe.)

Example—It is required to calculate the pipe size for a shallow-well suction pump having a capacity of 300 gals. per hour (see Fig. 8-1). The horizontal distance between the pump and the well is 75 ft. and the vertical lift is 20 ft. plus the 5 ft. below water level, as shown in the illustration.

Solution—Bearing in mind that 22 ft. is considered the maximum practical suction lift for a shallow-well pump, our calculation will be as follows:

Total water lift = 20 ft.

Total pipe friction loss assuming 5-gpm
flow through a 1-in. pipe.

Vertical part of pipe	= 25 ft.
Horizontal part of pipe	= 75 ft.
1-in. 90° elbow	= 6 ft.
Total footage	= 106 ft.

As noted in Table 8-1, the friction loss in a 1-in. pipe at 5 gals. per minute flow equals 3.25 ft. per 100 ft of pipe. Since there are 106 ft., the total friction loss = 106/100 × 3.25 = 1.06 × 3.25 = 3.4 ft. The total lift is 20 + 3.4, or 23.4 ft. As noted from our figures, a total lift of 23.4 ft. exceeds 22 ft. by a considerable margin, and although it is possible that an installation such as the foregoing will work, it should not be attempted as a practical solution.

If, on the other hand, a 1 ¼-in. pipe is selected, a similar reference to our friction-loss table indicates that the friction loss is reduced to 0.84 ft., making a total suction lift of 1.06 × 0.84 + 20 = 20.9 ft., which is within the practical suction limit.

Table 8-1. Friction Loss in Pipe

Flow	Size of Pipe											
Gals. per Min.	½ inch		¾ inch		1 inch		1 ¼ inch		1 ½ inch		2 inch	
	Ft.	Lbs.	Ft.	Lbs.	Ft.	Lbs.	Ft.	Lbs.	Ft.	Lbs.	Ft.	Lbs.
2	7.4	3.2	1.9	.82								
3	15.8	6.85	4.1	1.78	1.26	.55						
4	27.0	11.7	7.0	3.04	2.14	.93	.57	.25	.26	.11		
5	41.0	17.8	10.5	4.56	3.25	1.41	.84	.36	.40	.17		
6			14.7	6.36	4.55	1.97	1.20	.52	.56	.24	.20	.086
8			25.0	10.8	7.8	3.38	2.03	.88	.95	.41	.33	.143
10			38.0	16.4	11.7	5.07	1.32	1.43	.62	.50	.216	
12					16.4	7.10	4.3	1.86	2.01	.87	.70	.303
14					22.0	9.52	5.7	2.46	2.68	1.16	.94	.406
16					28.0	12.10	7.3	3.16	3.41	1.47	1.20	.520
18							9.1	3.94	4.24	1.83	1.49	.645

Example—It is necessary to install a shallow-well basement pumping system (see Fig. 8-2). The horizontal distance between pump and well is 300 ft. and the vertical lift is 15 ft. Determine the pipe size and pressure-switch setting for a 5-gpm pump.

Solution—With reference to our friction loss (Table 8-1), it will be noted that, if a 1-in. pipe is selected, a 5-gpm flow will cause a friction loss of 3.25 ft. per 100 ft. Since the total pipe length equals

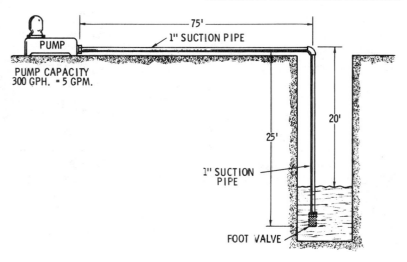

Fig. 8-1. A pipe arrangement for a shallow-well suction pump.

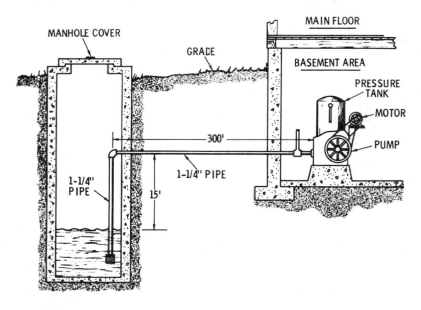

Fig. 8-2. Piping arrangement for a shallow-well basement pump.

197

3.25 ft. per 100 ft. Since the total pipe length equals 321 ft. (which figure includes the friction loss through the foot valve and elbow), we obtain a total friction loss of 3.25 × 3.21, or 10.43 ft. The total suction lift is therefore 15 + 10.43, or 25.43 ft. If, on the other hand, a 1 ¼-in. pipe is selected, a similar reference to the friction loss table will give a total loss of 0.84 × 3.21, or 2.7 ft. The total suction lift using the larger pipe will be 15 + 2.7, or 17.7 ft., which is the size that should be used for this particular installation.

In order to calculate the necessary pressure to overcome the 15-ft. elevation and pipe friction loss, the total suction lift value of 17.7 must be multiplied by 62.5/144 or 0.434; that is 17.7 × 0.434 equals 7.7 lbs. pressure. Pressure switches are usually set at 20 lbs. minimum and 40 lbs. maximum pressure. If 7.7 lbs. is added to the foregoing, we will arrive at a minimum switch setting of 27.7 and a maximum of 47.7 lbs.

Example—Water is to be pumped to a pressure tank (Fig. 8-3) in the basement of a home by an electric motor from a well in which the surface of the water is 85 ft. below the pump head. The tank is 15 ft. higher than the pump. Maximum pressure in the tank is 40 lbs. The distance from the well to the house is 170 ft. and 30 ft. of pipe is required in the house to reach the pressure tank. A 2 ½-in. drop pipe is being used between the well and the pump, and a 1 ¼-in. pipe from pump to tank. If it is assumed that a 480-gal. per hour pump is used in the installation, what size motor will be required?

Solution—In order to establish the motor size, it will first be necessary to calculate the total head of the pump installation. From the foregoing data we obtain:

Head due to difference in elevation = 2 × 2.03 = 4.06 ft.
Head due to pressure at tank = 85 + 15 = 100.00 ft.
Total pipe friction loss for the 200 feet of 1 ¼ in. pipe, assuming 8 gpm flow (from table) = 40 × 2.31 = 92.40 ft.
Total head = 196.46 ft.
(200 ft. approx.)

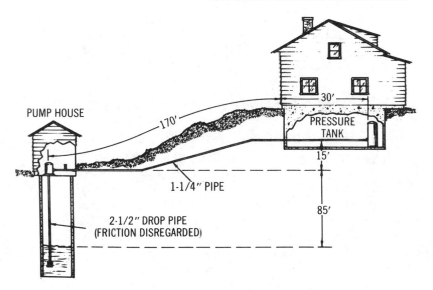

Fig. 8-3. Piping arrangement of a deep-well pumping system.

The theoretical horsepower required may be determined by multiplying the gallons per minute by the total head in feet and dividing the product by 33,000. Since the pump efficiency is not known, we may assume an arbitrary value for our deep-well pump as 30%.

The actual horsepower, therefore $= \dfrac{8 \times 8.34 \times 200}{33,000 \times 0.3} = 1\,\frac{1}{3}$

Use the next larger standard-size electric motor, which is $1\frac{1}{2}$ horsepower.

Example—A double-acting single-piston pump has a $2\frac{1}{2}$-in. diameter cylinder and a 3-in. stroke. What is the capacity per revolution?

Solution—In a problem of this type, it will first be necessary to calculate the piston area, which is $2.5^2 \times 0.7854$, or 4.909 sq. in. The pump capacity per stroke for one single-acting cylinder in

199

gallons is obviously 4.91 × 3/231, or 0.064. Since there is one forward-and-back stroke per revolution in a double-acting pump, the pump capacity per revolution is 0.064 × 2, or 0.128 gal.

EFFECT OF PIPE FRICTION LOSS

The friction loss in piping is a very important factor, and must be taken into account when evaluating a water distribution system. The friction loss shown in Table 8-1 is based on a section of 15-year-old pipe. With reference to this table, it is easy to determine the friction loss through any one of the pipe sizes shown for any flow of water. Thus, for example, a check in our friction-loss table indicates that discharge rate of 5 gallons per minute (gpm) through 100 ft. of 1-in. iron pipe results in a friction loss of 3.25 ft. The same gpm through 100 ft. of ¾-in. pipe will result in a friction loss of 10.5 ft. From this, it will be noted that pipe friction must be taken into consideration when pipe is selected for the suction line on a shallow-well pump, or for the discharge pipe from the pressure tank to the point of delivery.

PUMP CHARACTERISTICS

Automatic and semiautomatic pump installations for water supply purposes commonly employ three types of pumps. While each type has its individual characteristics, they all conform to the same general principles. There is the *reciprocating or plunger type*, the *rotary*, and the *centrifugal;* while the *jet* or *ejector* pump has derived its name from the introduction of a jet system attached to the centrifugal or reciprocating type of pump. A brief tabulation of the characteristics of the various types of pumps are given in Table 8-2. For convenience, they are listed as to speed, suction lift, and practical pressure head.

In the selection of pumps, it cannot be too strongly emphasized that since each pump application will differ, not only in capacity requirement but also in the pressure against which the pump will have to operate, plus other factors, the pump manufacturer should be consulted as to the type of pump that will be best suited for a particular installation.

For example: If a ½-in. hose with nozzle is to be used for sprinkling, water will be consumed at the rate of 200 gals. per hour. To permit use of water for other purposes at the same time, it is therefore essential to have a pump capacity in excess of 200 gals. per hour. Where ½-in. hose with nozzle is to be used, we recommend the use of a pump having a capacity of at least 220 gals. per hour, which leaves available for other uses water at the rate of 20

Table 8-2. Pump Characteristics

Type Pump	Speed	Practical Suction Lift	Pressure Head	Delivery Characteristics
Reciprocating: Shallow Well (low pressure) (medium pressure)	Slow 250 to 550 strokes per min.	22 to 25 ft.	40 to 43 lbs. Up to 100 lbs.	Pulsating (air chamber evens (pulsations) "
(high pressure) Deep Well	Slow 30 to 52 strokes per min.	Available for lifts up to 875 ft. Suction lift below cylinder 22 ft.	Up to 350 lbs. Normal 40 lbs.	" "
Rotary Pump: (shallow well)	400 to 1725 rpm	22 ft.	About 100 lbs.	Positive (slightly pulsating)
Ejector Pump: (shallow well and limited deep wells)	Used with centrifugal- turbine or shallow well reciprocating pump.	Max. around 120 ft. Practical at lifts of 80 ft. or less	40 lbs. (normal) Available at up to 70 lbs. pressure head	Continuous nonpul- sating, high capac- ity with low-pres- sure head
Centrifugal: Shallow Well (single stage)	High, 1750 and 3600 rpm	15 ft. maximum	40 lbs. (normal) 70 lbs. (maximum)	Continuous nonpul- sating, high capac- ity with low-pres- sure head
Turbine Type: (single impeller)	High, 1750 rpm	28 ft. maximum at sea level	40 lbs. (normal) Available up to 100 lbs. pressure head	Continuous nonpul- sating, high capac- ity with low-pres- sure head

gals. per hour when the hose is being used. In determining the desired pump capacity, even for ordinary requirements, it is advisable to select a size large enough so that the pump will not run more than a few hours per day at the most.

Reciprocating pumps will deliver water in quantities proportional to the number of strokes and the length and size of the

201

cylinder. They are adapted to a wide range of speeds, and to practically any depth of well. Since reciprocating pumps are positive in operation, they should be fitted with automatic relief valves to prevent rupture of pipes or other damage, should power be applied against abnormal pressure.

If it is not practical to set the pump directly over the well, as is necessary with deep-well plunger pumps, an ejector-type pump may be selected. The ejector pump is most efficient where the lift is between 25 and 65 ft., but will operate with lifts of up to 120 ft. The ejector pump, however, is not usually recommended for wells with depth in excess of 80 ft.

Centrifugal pumps are somewhat critical as to speed and should be used only where power can be applied at a reasonable constant speed. Vertical-type centrifugal pumps are used in deep wells. They are usually driven through shafting by vertical motors mounted at the top of the well. Rather large wells are required for either centrifugal or turbine deep-well pumps, the size depending on the capacity and design of the pump. Centrifugal pumps are efficient in higher capacities, but in the lower capacities of 10 gals. or less per minute, their efficiency is not as high as that of the plunger pumps. It is usually not practical to adopt centrifugal pumps for installations requiring small volumes of water.

Turbine pumps as used in domestic water systems are self-priming. Their smooth operation makes them suitable for applications where noise and vibration must be kept at a minimum.

Ejector pumps are becoming very popular. They operate quietly, and neither the deep-well nor the shallow-well type need to be mounted over the well.

CHAPTER 9

Questions and Answers for Plumbers

As mentioned earlier in this book, plumbers are called on to know a wide variety of information. What follows is a series of questions designed to evaluate the depth and degree of an individual's knowledge. The answers, it should be noted, are based on common practice. Individual communities or jurisdictions may have different requirements, and if so, these must be abided by.

What is meant by plumbing?
Answer: It is the art of installing the pipes, fixtures, and other apparatus in buildings for bringing in the water supply and removing liquid and water-carried wastes.

What constitutes the plumbing system of a building?
Answer: It includes the water-supply distributing pipes, the fixtures and fixture traps, the soil, waste, and vent pipes, the house drain and house sewer, the storm-water drainage, all with their

devices, appurtenances, and connections within and adjacent to the building.

What is a water service pipe?

Answer: It is the pipe from the water main to the building served.

What is meant by water distribution pipes?

Answer: They are the pipes that carry water from the service pipes to the plumbing fixtures.

What are plumbing fixtures?

Answer: These are receptacles intended to receive and discharge water, liquid, or water-carried wastes into a drainage system.

Why must all plumbing fixtures be connected to a water source?

Answer: In order that they be provided with a sufficient amount of water to keep them in a serviceable and sanitary condition.

What is a trap?

Answer: A fitting or device constructed to prevent the passage of air or gas through a pipe without materially affecting the flow of sewage or waste water through it.

What is meant by the vent pipes?

Answer: Any pipe provided to ventilate a house drainage system and to prevent trap siphonage and back pressure.

What is a local ventilating pipe?

Answer: A pipe through which foul air is removed from a room or a fixture.

What is a soil pipe?

Answer: Any pipe which carries the discharge of water closets, with or without the discharges from other fixtures, to the house drain.

What is a waste pipe?

Answer: A pipe that receives the discharge of any fixture except water closets, and carries it to the house drain, soil, or waste stacks.

What is a main?

Answer: The main of any system of horizontal, vertical, or continuous piping is the part of the system that receives the wastes and vents or back vents from fixture outlets or traps directly or through branch pipes.

What is meant by branch piping?

Answer: The part of the system that extends horizontally at a slight grade, with or without lateral or vertical extensions or vertical arms, from the main to receive fixture outlets not directly connected to the main.

What is a stack?

Answer: Stack is a general term for any vertical line of soil, waste, or vent piping.

What is meant by a building drain?

Answer: The part of the lowest horizontal piping of a house drainage system that receives the discharge from soil, waste, and other drainage pipes inside the walls of any building and carries it to the house sewer beginning 5 ft. outside of the inner face of the building wall.

What is a building sewer?

Answer: It is that part of the horizontal piping of a building drainage system extending from the house drain 5 ft. outside of the inner face of the building wall to its connection with the main sewer and conveying the drainage from one building site.

What is a dead end?

Answer: A branch leading from a soil, waste, vent, house drain, or house sewer, which is terminated at a developed distance of 2 ft. or more by means of a cap, plug, or other fitting not used for admitting water to the pipe.

What are the rules as to workmanship and materials?

205

Answer: All work must be performed in a thorough, workman-like manner, and all material used in any drainage or plumbing system or part thereof must be free from defects.

How is it possible to determine if the pipes used are of the proper size and weight?
Answer: The length of each pipe, fitting, trap, fixture, and device used in a plumbing or drainage system should be stamped or indelibly marked with the weight or quality, and the maker's mark or name.

When may the house sewer be of earthenware pipe?
Answer: Only when a proper foundation can be obtained consisting of a natural bed of earth, rock, etc.

What kind of material must be used in main, soil, waste, or vent pipes?
Answer: Main, soil, waste, and vent pipes can be made of whatever local codes allow, usually cast iron, steel, copper, or plastic.

What is mean by the term riser lines in a plumbing system?
Answer: The term *riser* is generally applied to the vertical pipes extending through the building from its connection with the house main.

May cast-iron pipe be used in a plumbing system?
Answer: Yes, if the cast-iron pipe conforms to the standard specifications of the American Society for Testing Materials.

What are the requirements when brass and copper pipe is used?
Answer: All brass and copper pipe shall conform to the standard specifications of the A.S.T.M.

How should a caulked joint be made?
Answer: All caulked joints should be firmly packed with oakum or hemp, and secured only with pure lead not less than 1 in. deep, well caulked. No paint, varnish, or putty should be used until the joint is tested.

How is an approved joint in lead pipe or between lead and brass or copper pipe made?

Answer: Joints in lead pipe, or between lead pipe and brass or copper pipe, ferrules, soldering nipples, bushings or traps, in all cases on the sewer side of the trap, and in concealed joints on the inlet side of the trap, should be full-wiped joints with an exposed surface of the solder to each side of the joint of not less than ¾ in., and a minimum thickness at the thickest part of the joint of not less than ⅜ in.; or by use of a lead-to-iron union.

What are the requirements when joints are made between lead and cast or wrought iron?

Answer: The joints shall be made by means of a caulking ferrule, soldering nipple, or bushings.

When should slip joints and unions be used?

Answer: Slip joints should be permitted only in trap seals or on the inlet side of the trap. Unions on the sewer side of the trap should be ground faced and should not be concealed or enclosed.

What is the term used for a fitting that makes an angle between two adjacent pipes?

Answer: Elbow.

What is the name used for a fitting that has one side outlet at right angles to the run?

Answer: Tee.

What is the name for a fitting having a larger size at one end than on the other?

Answer: Reducer.

What is the name of a fitting which has one side outlet at any angle other than 90°?

Answer: Wye.

What is the term generally employed for a piece of pipe threaded on both ends and not more than 12 in. long?

Answer: Nipple.

207

What should be the minimum distance between the hot- and cold-water risers in a plumbing system?

Answer: The distance between the hot- and cold-water risers where a hot-water supply is installed should not be less than 6 in., and where conditions encountered are such that they cannot be readily placed 6 in. or more apart, the hot-water riser should be covered with an approved insulating material so it doesn't interfere with the prompt delivery of hot water to the faucet when required.

What is the minimum size of a main vent pipe?

Answer: The size of a main vent pipe must never be less than 2 in. in diameter.

How are the required sizes of vent pipes determined?

Answer: The size of main vents or vent stacks should be determined from the size of the soil or waste stack vented and the total number of units drained into it. However, they must not be less than the following: for water closets on three or more floors, 3 in. in diameter; for other fixtures where the building is less than 7 floors in height, 2 in. in diameter; where the building is less than 9 stories in height, 3 in. in diameter; from 8 to 16 stories and less in height, 4 in. in diameter; etc. For all fixtures other than water closets and slop sinks, and for buildings more than 8 stories in height, the vent pipes may be 1 in. smaller in diameter than the above.

Where should a clean-out be placed in a vertical waste or soil stack?

Answer: A clean-out that is easily accessible should be installed at the foot of each vertical waste or soil stack.

How should waste or soil pipes be protected against obstruction?

Answer: By the use of strong metallic strainers placed over the outlets.

Should each building have soil and waste stacks?

Answer: Yes. Every building in which plumbing fixtures are installed should have a soil and waste stack extending full size through the roof.

How far above the roof should soil or vent pipe lines be carried?
Answer: All roof extensions of soil and vent stacks should be run full size at least 6 in. above the roof coping, and when the roof is used for other purposes than weather protection, such extension should not be less than 5 ft. above the roof.

Should special rules apply to soil and vent pipes used in a cold climate?
Answer: Where there is danger of frost closing it, no roof extension should be less than 3 in. in diameter. The change in diameter must be accomplished by the use of a long increase at least 1 ft. below the roof, and where the access to the roof is difficult, a test opening should be provided at this point.

May a vent or soil pipe be terminated within a distance of 2 ft. from any door, window, scuttle, or air shaft?
Answer: No. The roof terminal or any stack or vent, if within 10 ft. of any door, window, scuttle, or air shaft, should extend at least 3 ft. above the same.

May soil or vent lines be carried outside of buildings?
Answer: No soil or vent lines should be installed or permitted outside of a building unless adequate provision is made to protect them from frost.

Where should main vents be connected?
Answer: All main vents or vent stacks should connect full size at their base to the main soil or vent pipe at or below the lowest fixture branch, and should extend undiminished in size above the roof, and should be reconnected with the main soil or waste vent at least 3 ft. above the highest fixture branch.

When offsets are made in vent lines, how should they be connected?
Answer: All vent and branch vent lines should be connected and installed so that they are free from drops or sags, and be graded

209

and connected to drip back to the soil or waste pipe by gravity. Where the vent pipes connect to a horizontal soil or waste pipe, the vent branch shall be taken off above the center line of the pipe, and the vent pipes must rise vertically, or at an angle of 45°, to a point 6 in. above the fixture it is venting before offsetting horizontally or connecting to the branch, main waste, or soil vent.

When may circuit or loop vents be employed?
Answer: A circuit or loop vent is permitted as follows: A branch soil or waste pipe to which two and not more than eight water closets, pedestal urinals, trap standards, slop sinks, or shower stalls are connected in series, may be vented by a circuit or loop vent, which should be taken off in front of the last fixture connection. Where fixtures discharge above such branches, each branch should be provided with a relief one-half the diameter of the soil or waste stack, taken off in front of the first fixture connection.

What is the required running diameter of traps for urinals?
Answer: 1½ in. (minimum).

What are the requirements for a permissible trap?
Answer: Every trap should be self-cleaning. All traps used for bath tubs, lavatories, sinks, and other similar fixtures should be of brass, cast iron, galvanized malleable iron, or porcelain enameled inside. Galvanized or porcelain enameled traps should be extra heavy and have a full-bore smooth-interior waterway, with threads tapped out of solid metal. Some local codes allow the use of plastic materials and traps.

Where should the fixture trap be placed relative to its fixture?
Answer: The trap should be as close to the fixture as possible, but not more than 24 in. from the fixture.

What are the requirements in regard to clean-outs in fixture traps?
Answer: All traps, except water-closet traps, should be provided with an accessible brass trap screw of ample size, protected by the water seal.

210

May fixture traps be connected in series?
Answer: No. The discharge from any fixture should never pass through more than one trap on its way to the house drain.

Must all fixture traps be protected against back pressure and siphonage?
Answer: Yes. Every fixture trap should be protected against siphonage and back pressure, and air circulation assured by means of a soil or waste stack vent, a continuous waste or soil vent, or a loop or circuit vent. No crown vent should be installed.

Must trap levels be protected against frost and evaporation?
Answer: All traps should be installed true with respect to their water seals and protected from frost and evaporation.

What is the seal of a trap?
Answer: It is the depth of the water between the dip and the outlet of the trap. The effectiveness of a trap always depends on its water seal.

What is the dip of a trap?
Answer: The part of a trap that dips into the seal, and under which all waste matter must pass.

What is meant by the term siphonage?
Answer: By referring to an "S" trap, it will be readily seen that the outlet forms a perfect siphon; the part of the trap between the dip and the outlet forming the short side, and the waste pipe from the outlet downward forming the long side. When a large quantity of water is discharged from the fixture into the trap, the water fills the entire trap and waste pipe for some distance below the trap. It can be seen that the weight of the water is much greater at the outlet side than at the inlet side of the trap, and it tends to cause the water in the trap to rise to the outlet and follow the larger body of water in the waste pipe, leaving the trap without any water to form its water seal.

What determines the resistance against siphonage in a trap?

211

Answer: The depth of the water seal determines the amount of resistance a trap will offer to being unsealed by siphonage.

How should service pipes be protected when exposed to frost?
Answer: They should be protected by a sufficient amount of felt or other insulation and supported by metal sleeves or approved metal bands.

What precautions should be taken when thawing a frozen water pipe.
Answer: If the thawing is done with a blow torch or hot water, the thawing medium should be applied to the water-supply end of the pipe, opening a faucet if possible to indicate when the flow of water starts. It is well to keep in mind that the middle of the pipe should never be thawed first, because expansion of the water confined by ice on both sides may burst the pipe.

How should a waste or sewer pipe be thawed out?
Answer: When thawing a waste or sewer pipe, always work upward from the lower end, to permit the water to drain away.

Briefly discuss the most effective methods used to thaw out frozen water pipes.
Answer: The method to be used will be determined by the amount of pipe to be thawed, as well as the size and location. For short lengths of exposed pipe, boiling hot water or hot cloths have proven to be effective. If there is no danger of fire, or if the necessary precautions against fire are observed, a blow torch or burning newspaper run back and forth along the frozen water pipe gives quick results. When the pipe to be thawed is located underground, or is otherwise inaccessible, the pipe should be disconnected at the house end and boiling water poured through the opening, using a small piece of auxiliary pipe or rubber tubing to which a funnel conveniently is attached. When a long section of inaccessible piping or leaders are to be thawed, low-voltage electricity has been found to be effective, particularly with electric heating cables. Electric blankets have been used with success as well.

What is the amount of water required for a water closet or pedestal urinal for one flushing?

Answer: All water closets or pedestal urinals should be flushed with an approved tank or flush valve having a flushing capacity of at least 4 gals. for water closets, and at least 2 gals. for urinals, and should be properly adjusted to prevent water waste.

What are the causes of sewer obstruction, and how should sewers be constructed to lessen this trouble?

Answer: Causes may be any one of the following: broken pipes, insufficient grade to give cleansing velocities, newspaper, rags, garbage or other solids in the sewage, congealing of grease in pipes and house sewer traps, and poor joint construction whereby root-lets grow into the sewer and choke it. The proper grade and good construction, with particular care given to the joints, will avert or lessen these troubles. The sewer should be made perfectly straight with the interior of the joints scraped or swabbed smooth. When the joint-filling material has set, the hollows beneath the hubs should be filled with good earth free of stones, well tamped or puddled in place. It is important that like material be used at the sides of the pipe and above it for at least one foot.

What is a siphon chamber and how does it work?

Answer: The purpose of a siphon chamber is to secure intermit-tent discharge, thus allowing a considerable period of time for one dose to work off in the soil and for air to enter the soil spaces before another flush is received. It is also used to secure distribu-tion over a larger area and in a more even manner than where the sewage is allowed to dribble and produce the conditions of the old-fashioned sink drain, namely, a small area of water-logged ground.

Three types of sewage siphons are shown in Fig. 9-1. In all, the essential principle is the same. A column of air is entrapped between two columns of water; when the water in the chamber rises to a predetermined height, called the discharge line, the pressure forces out the confined air, upsetting the balance and causing a rush of water through to the sewer. The entire operation is fully automatic and very simple. The siphons shown are com-mercial products and are made of cast iron. Their simplicity and

213

reliability are enhanced by the small number of nonmovable parts. Manufacturers furnish information for setting the siphons and putting them in operation. For example, for type 2 in Fig. 9-1: (1) set siphon trap (U-shaped pipe) plumb, making E (height from floor to top of long leg) as specified; (2) fill siphon trap with water till it begins to run out at B; (3) place bell in position at top of long leg, and the siphon is ready for service. Do not fill vent pipe on side of bell. The overhead siphon (type 3, Fig. 9-1) may be installed readily in a tank already built by the addition of an outlet pump. If properly set and handled, sewage siphons require very little attention and flush with certainty. However, like all plumbing fixtures, they are subject to stoppage if rags, newspapers, and similar solids get into the sewage. If fouling of the sniffling hole or vent prevents the entrance of sufficient air into the bell to lock the siphon properly, allowing sewage to dribble through, the remedy is to clean the siphon. It is well to remember that siphons are for handling only liquid; sludge, if allowed to accumulate, will choke them.

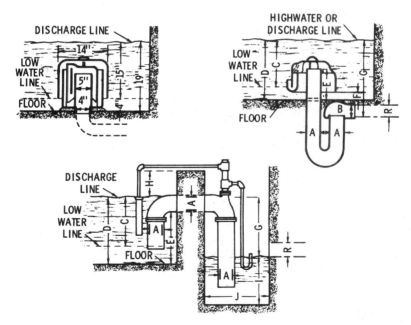

Fig. 9-1. Three types of sewer siphon systems.

Is it necessary to have a plumbing system tested and inspected after completion, and who should make the test?

Answer: The entire plumbing system should be tested by the plumber in the presence of a plumbing inspector, or the proper administrative authority, to ensure compliance with all the requirements of the plumbing regulations, and to ensure that the installation and construction of the system is in accordance with the approved plans and the permit.

How is this test accomplished?

Answer: By filling all the piping of the plumbing system with water or air. After the plumbing fixtures have been set and their traps filled with water, the entire drainage system should be submitted to the final air-pressure test. The proper administrative authority may require the removal of any clean-outs to ascertain if the pressure has reached all parts of the system.

How should the water test be made?

Answer: The water test may be applied to the drainage system in its entirety or in sections. If applied to the entire system, all openings in the piping should be tightly closed, except the highest opening above the roof, and the system filled with water to the point of overflow above the roof. If the system is tested in sections, each opening should be tightly plugged, except the highest opening of the section under test, and each section filled with water; but no section should be tested with less than a 10-ft. head of water or with less than 5 lbs. of air pressure. In testing successive sections, at least the upper 10 ft. of the next preceding section should be retested, so that no joint or pipe in the building is tested for less than a 10-ft. head of water or 5 lbs. of air pressure.

How should the air test be made?

Answer: By attaching the air compressor or test apparatus to any suitable opening, and closing all other air inlets and outlets to the system, then forcing air into the system until there is uniform pressure of 5 pounds per square inch (psi), or sufficient to balance a 10-in. column of mercury.

215

How long should this air pressure be maintained in the drainage system?

Answer: For at least 15 minutes.

How should the final air test be made?

Answer: In the final air test, the air machine should be connected to any suitable opening or outlet, and air pressure equivalent to a 1-in. water column should be applied and left standing at least 15 minutes. If there is no leakage or forcing of trap seals indicated by the fluctuation of the drum, float, or water column, the system is airtight.

In what order may the tests be made?

Answer: Separately, or as follows: 1. The house sewer and all its branches from the property line to the house drain. 2. The house drain and yard drains, including all piping to the height of 10 ft. above the highest point on the house drain, except the exposed connections to fixtures. 3. The soil, waste, vent, inside conductor, and drainage pipe which should be covered up before the building is enclosed or ready for completion. (The test required for 2 and 3 may be combined.) 4. The final test of the whole system. 5. After each of the tests has been made, the proper administrative authority shall issue a written approval.

What is a relief valve?

Answer: It is a valve arranged to provide an automatic relief in case of excess pressure.

What is a safety valve?

Answer: It is a relief valve for expansive fluids and is provided with a chamber to control the amount of blow-back before the valve reseats.

What is a stop valve?

Answer: It is a valve of the globe type used to shut off a line.

What is a back-pressure valve?

Answer: It is a valve similar to a low-pressure safety valve that is set to maintain a certain back pressure on feed operating pressure irrespective of pressure variations of the supply. The back-pressure valve is arranged to relieve any excess supply to the atmosphere or elsewhere, and it opens and closes automatically as required to produce this result.

What is means by the term electrolysis?
Answer: It is generally applied to electrolytic corrosion due to electric current conduction by water, gas mains, or metallic structures.

Where does electrolysis take place?
Answer: Along water mains or metallic structures, where the electric stray current leaves the metal for the ground or some other conductor of less resistance.

Where is the electrolytic corrosion most common?
Answer: In densely populated areas along electric railroad lines where track rails are utilized as a negative return circuit.

How can electrolysis be avoided or lessened?
Answer: By lowering the voltage drop, which is done by increasing the metallic area of the negative return circuits adjacent to the water mains. In some cases, insulating or installing high-resistance pipe joints have been found to limit the conduction of stray electrical currents.

How may an electric current be detected in a main?
Answer: By means of a sensitive galvanometer, which can be calibrated to show the potential drop along the pipe, measuring the distance, and calculating the cross-sectional area. The potential drop divided by the resistance gives the flow of current in the main. By knowing the direction of the flow, its amount, and the efficiency of corrosion, the actual damage being done by electrolysis may be calculated as a definite weight of metal per annum.

What are the essential requirements of piping and apparatus for fire protection?
Answer: It must be capable of producing, without question, the

217

desired performance, and it must be designed to function invariably, regardless of age or weather conditions.

Who establishes rules for all kinds of fire protective apparatus?
Answer: The National Board of Fire Underwriters and allied organizations.

How should the piping for an automatic sprinkler system be designed?
Answer: It must be designed so as to ensure: (1) an adequate and reliable water supply, (2) ample and complete distribution, (3) proper protection against freezing.

What are the rules in regard to sprinkler system water supply?
Answer: It is generally considered necessary to have two sources of water supply, one which should require no manual operation. For example, a common arrangement is a gravity tank in combination with a fire-department connection to be used when the apparatus arrives.

What are the N.B.F.U. rules in regards to location and spacing of sprinkler heads?
Answer: They take into account the type of building construction and the dimension of the bays. In general, one sprinkler head is required for each 80 to 100 sq. ft. of floor area.

What is the relation between the number of heads and branch pipes?
Answer: Piping should be so arranged that the number of heads on any branch pipe does not exceed eight.

What should be the size of riser lines in a sprinkler system?
Answer: Each riser in a sprinkler system should be of sufficient size to supply all the sprinklers connected to it on any one floor, or if there is no approved fire stop between the floors, the riser should be of sufficient size to accommodate the total number of sprinklers.

Must riser and supply lines be protected against frost?
Answer: If in exposed locations, they must be adequately protected against frost by means of insulating materials.

What type of valves may be used on a fire-protective system?
Answer: All valves must be of the O.S. & Y. pattern, and check valves should be installed in all sources of supply. Each system should be provided with a gate valve located to control all sources of water supply except that from fire-departmental sources.

What is a *dry system,* and where is such a system required?
Answer: It is a system in which the piping is ordinarily filled with air at a pressure considerably lower than water pressure. When a sprinkler head opens, water enters the system and drives the air out ahead of it. This type of system is required in rooms that cannot be properly heated.

What is the most important feature of the dry system?
Answer: It is the dry-pipe valve, a device that normally prevents water from entering the system but that opens when the air pressure is lowered due to the opening of a head.

What is the water source for an automatic sprinkler system?
Answer: A municipal system under pressure or overhead gravity tanks are used for automatic sprinklers and hose connections.

How are the required tank sizes determined?
Answer: The size of a tank for a given service is determined individually by the insurance authorities. In general, when feeding sprinklers, the tank must have a capacity of 10,000 to 25,000 gals. When feeding both sprinklers and hose, a minimum capacity of 30,000 gals. is usually required.

What is the size of discharge pipes relative to tank capacity in an elevated gravity-tank system?
Answer: Elevated gravity tanks must have a discharge pipe of not less than 6 in. for tank sizes up to 25,000 gals. capacity, and generally not less than 8 in. for 30,000 up to 110,000 gals., and 10 in. for greater capacities.

How are the tanks protected against freezing?

Answer: The usual arrangement consists of a tubular steam heater to which a connection is made from the base of the tank discharge pipe. The heated water is carried up to the tank by a separate pipe. This arrangement permits the temperature of the coldest water to be observed readily and is by far the simplest and most reliable method. The coldest water should not be allowed to be below 40° F.

What are the regulations in regard to pressure tanks?

Answer: Pressure tanks for fire service are ordinarily kept two-thirds full of water, and with an air pressure on the surface of the water of 75 lbs. plus three times the pressure caused by the column of water in the sprinkler system above the tank bottom.

What is the capacity of pressure tanks?

Answer: The capacity is usually set by the insurance inspection authorities having jurisdiction, and is usually between 4,500 and 9,000 gals. per tank.

How should a pressure tank be designed?

Answer: It should be in accordance with the rules for unfired pressure vessels of the A.S.M.E.

What determines the use of house supply tanks?

Answer: When the water pressure is not sufficient to supply all fixtures freely and continuously, a house supply tank should be provided. The tank should be adequate to supply all fixtures at all times.

What methods should be used to supply house tanks?

Answer: Tanks should be supplied from the street pressure or, when necessary, by power pumps. When such tanks are supplied from the street pressure, ball cocks should be provided.

Where should the water supply inlet to roof tanks be located?

Answer: Water supply inlets to roof tanks should be located at least 2 in. above the overflow pipe level of the tank and should be equipped with an automatic ball stop. The outlet from a roof tank to the distribution system in the building should be effectively equipped to prevent solids from entering into such piping. All down-feed supplies from a tank, cross connected in any manner with distribution supply piping in a building supplied by direct street main or pump pressure, should be equipped with a check valve to prevent back flow of water into the roof tank.

May a gravity tank be directly connected to the city water main?

Answer: No gravity tank should be directly connected to the city water main, but should be provided with an over-the-rim filler, the orifice of the outlet of which must be elevated a distance equal to the least diameter of such water-discharging orifice or outlet, and in no case less than 1 in. above the top rim of the tank.

What size discharge pipe should be provided for a gravity tank having a capacity of 500 gals. or more?

Answer: The discharge pipe from a gravity tank of 500 gals. or more capacity should be at least 4 in. nominal diameter for a distance of not less than 4 ft., and in no case should it be smaller than the main section of the riser. The shut-off valve should be the same size as the outlet from the tank, but not less than a 4-in. gate valve.

What are the rules as to the tightness of plumbing joints and connections?

Answer: Joints and connections shall be made gas and water tight.

What type of joints is required in vitrified clay pipes?

Answer: Joints in vitrified clay sewer pipe should be firmly packed with oakum or hemp and should be secured with cement, mortar, or asphaltic compound at least 1 in. thick.

How should caulked joints be made?

Answer: Brass caulking ferrules should be either of the best quality of cast brass or should be of the cold-drawn seamless tube variety, with weights and dimensions in accordance with Table 9-1. Soldering nipples should be of brass pipe (iron-pipe size) or heavy cast brass of at least the weight shown in Table 9-1. Solder-

Table 9-1. Weight of Soldering Nipples

Pipe Size (inches)	Actual inside diameter (inches)	Length (inches)	Weight	
			Pounds	Ounces
2.......	2¼	4½	1	...
3.......	3¼	4½	1	12
4.......	4¼	4½	2	8

ing bushings shall be of brass pipe (iron-pipe size) or heavy brass or copper.

What type of screw joints should be made in a plumbing system?

Answer: Screw joints should be tapered with the threads sharp and true, and all burrs due to cutting reamed out smooth. Where fitting compounds, red lead, white lead, or other joint materials are used in making up threaded joints, such materials should be applied to the male threads only.

What type of wiped solder joints should be made in a plumbing system?

Answer: Joints in lead pipes, brass or copper pipes, ferrules, soldering nipples, bushings, or traps, should be full-wiped joints, either manufactured or made in the field. An exposed surface of the solder at least ¾ in. with a minimum thickness at the thickest part of the joint of ⅜ in. should be on each side of the joint. It is unlawful to use overcast or cup joints.

What are the rules for making joints of lead to cast iron, steel, or wrought iron?

Answer: Joints of lead to cast iron, steel, or wrought iron, should be made by means of a caulking ferrule, soldering nipple, or bushing.

What type of fixture flanges should be used in a plumbing system?

Answer: Flanges to receive fixture outlets should be at least ³⁄₁₆ in. thick and should be made of brass or cast iron. (Some plumbing codes allow the use of plastic pipe.)

QUESTIONS AND ANSWERS FOR PLUMBERS

What are the rules for connections between drainage pipes and water closets, pedestal urinal and trap, and standard slop sinks in a plumbing system?

Answer: The connections between drainage pipes and water closets, floor outlets, slop sinks, pedestal urinals, and earthenware trap standards should be made by means of flanges caulked to the drainage pipes. Such connections may be wiped or soldered to lead pipes. Such connections should be bolted to the earthenware with an approved gasket or washer between the earthenware and the connection. Floor outlet connections should be set on an approved floor slab or ring made of materials impervious to moisture.

When are slip joints and unions permitted?

Answer: Slip joints or unions are permitted only in trap seals or on the inlet side of the trap, except where it is impracticable to otherwise provide for expansion in stacks of unusual height. The authorities may permit the use of an approved type of expansion joint that comprises, in part, a slip joint.

What are the rules as to roof joint connections in a plumbing system?

Answer: Where the pipes pass through roofs, the joints should be made watertight.

When are expansion and contraction of piping due to temperature variations provided for in a plumbing system?

Answer: In structures over 150 ft. high, adequate means should be provided for taking care of the expansion and contraction of all vertical lines of pipe.

What is the rule for protection of soil or waste stacks?

Answer: Soil or waste stacks should be installed inside the structure.

What plumbing connections are prohibited?

Answer: It is unlawful to make any waste connection to a bend of a water closet or similar fixture. It is unlawful to use soil or waste vents as soil or waste pipes.

223

What are the rules for changes in direction in a plumbing system?

Answer: Changes in direction should be made by the appropriate use of 45° wyes, half wyes, long-sweep ¼ bends, ⅙, ⅛, or ¹⁄₁₆ bends, or long-turn tee-wye fittings, except that short-turn tee-wye fittings may be used on vertical stacks. Fittings other than these may be used if such fittings are approved in accordance with the rules of the authorities. All ¼ bends shall be of the long-turn type. Tees and crosses may be used in vent pipes.

What grade or slope is required in horizontal drainage piping?

Answer: Horizontal drainage piping should be run in practical alignment and at a uniform grade of at least ⅛ in. per foot for 4-in. pipe and larger, and ¼ in. per foot for 3-in. pipe and smaller.

May old house drains and sewers be connected to a new structure?

Answer: Old house drains and sewers may be used for connections to new structures or new plumbing only when such drains and sewers are found, on examination, to conform in all respects to the requirements of the authorities.

What is meant by *fixture unit,* and how was this term derived?

Answer: The unit system was formulated from tests conducted a number of years ago by the subcommittee on plumbing of the Building Code Committee under the Department of Commerce. Standard plumbing fixtures were installed and individually tested, and the amount of liquid waste which could be discharged through their outlet orifices in a given interval was carefully measured.

During the test it was found that a wash basin, which is one of the smaller plumbing fixtures, would discharge waste in the amount of approximately 7½ gals. of water per minute. Since 1 cu. ft. contains 7.4805 gals., it will be observed that this volume was so close to a cubic foot of water that the committee decided to establish it as a basis of the unit system and termed the discharge of the wash basin as one fixture unit. Therefore, one fixture unit represents approximately 7½ gals. of water.

What are the values in fixture units for common plumbing fixtures?

Answer: Table 9-2 is based on the rate of discharge from a wash basin or lavatory as the unit employed to determine fixture equivalents.

Table 9-2. Fixture Unit Values

Fixture	Units
Lavatory or wash basin	1
Kitchen sink	1½
Bathtub	2
Laundry tub	2
Combination fixture	3
Urinal	3
Shower bath	3
Floor drain	2
Slop sink	4
Water closet	6
One bathroom group (consisting of water closet, lavatory, bathtub, and overhead shower, or water closet, lavatory, and shower compartment)	8
180 square feet of roof drained	1

What determines the size of waste outlets in fixtures?

Answer: The size of waste outlets in fixtures is determined by the type and number of fixtures installed. Table 9-3 gives the approximate size of waste outlets for various numbers of fixture units.

Table 9-3. Waste Sizes for Various Fixture Units

Size of waste outlet in fixtures	Number of units
½ inch, ¾ inch, less than 1 inch	½
1 inch	1
1¼ inches	2
1½ inches	3
2 inches	5½
2½ inches	8
3 inches	15
4 inches	30
5 inches	50
6 inches	80
8 inches	160

What are the requirements for roof extensions of soil and waste stacks?

Answer: Roof extensions of soil and waste stacks or roof vents should be run at full size at least 1 ft. above any roof pitched at an angle of 30° or more from the horizontal. They should be full size at least 5 ft. where the roof is used for any purpose other than weather protection. If the roof terminal of any vent, soil, or waste pipe is within 10 ft. of any door, window, scuttle, or airshaft, the terminal should extend at least 3 ft. above the opening.

When soil, waste, or vent pipes are extended through the roof, they should be at least 3 in. Pipes smaller than 3 in. should be provided with a proper increaser located just below the roof line.

What are the minimum sizes of individual soil and waste branches?

Answer: Minimum sizes of soil or waste branches to individual fixtures should be in accordance with Table 9-4. The size of any stack, building drain, or house sewer should be at least that of the largest branch connected to it.

What determines the size of branch soils and wastes in a plumbing system?

Answer: The required size of branch soils and wastes receiving the discharge of two or more fixtures should be determined on the

Table 9-4. Soil and Waste Branch Sizes for Various Fixtures

Fixture	Branch Size	
Water closet	3	inches
Floor drains	3	inches
Urinal	2	inches
Slop sink	3	inches
Sink, except slop sink	2	inches
Bathtub	1½	inches
Laundry tray	1½	inches
Shower bath	2	inches
Lavatory	1½	inches
Drinking fountain	1½	inches
Dental cuspidor	1½	inches
Sterilizers with ½-inch waste outlet	1½	inches
Combination fixture, laundry tubs, and kitchen sinks	2	inches

basis of the total number of fixture units drained by branch soils and wastes, in accordance with Table 9-5.

Table 9-5. Size of Piping for Branch and Soil Wastes

Maximum number of fixture units permitted	Maximum number of water closets permitted	Diameter of branch (inches)
2	.....	1½
9	.....	2
20	.....	2½
35	1	3
100	11	4
250	28	5

What are the minimum size waste stacks required for water closets?

Answer: No water closet should discharge into a stack less than 3 in. in diameter. Not more than one water closet should be permitted to discharge into a 3-in. stack or branch.

What are the rules for installation of oil separators?

Answer: When the liquid wastes from any structure consist wholly or in part of volatile, inflammable oil, and an oil separator is required by law, the fixtures receiving such wastes should be connected to an independent drainage system discharging into such a separator. Every oil separator should have an individual 3-in. vent extending from the top of such separator to the outer air at a point at least 12 ft. above street level. The discharge from the oil separator should be either independently connected to the sewer or to the sewer side of the house trap.

A fresh-air inlet should be provided from the drain at the inlet side of the separator to the outer air, and such inlet should terminate with the open end at least 6 in. above grade. The diameter of the inlet pipe should be equal to the diameter of such drain, but in any case, such diameter should be 3 in. or more. The horizontal drain and one riser should be at least 3 in. diameter. Risers should be carried full size through the roof. Oil separators should be installed in accordance with rules of the authorities.

What are the rules as to the discharge of acid in a plumbing system?

Answer: It is unlawful to discharge into the regular plumbing system any acids or liquids of any kind which may be injurious to such a system. Such acids or liquids should be discharged through an independent system directly to the sewer. Piping for both drainage and vents should be of acid-resisting material approved by the authorities.

The authorities may, however, permit the discharge into the regular plumbing system of chemically neutralized acid waste or other liquids which would otherwise be injurious to the system if, in their opinion, the treatment of these liquids renders them no more harmful than regular waste and drainage.

May waste from an oil storage plant be connected to a public drain or sewer?

Answer: It is unlawful to connect an oil storage plant with any public drain or sewer, or to permit any liquid product of petroleum to escape into any such drain or sewer.

How should drainage of yard areas and roofs be accomplished?

Answer: Yard areas, courts, and courtyards (if paved), together with all roofs, should be drained into a storm sewer. See Table 9-6.

How should vent pipes be graded?

Answer: Vent and branch vent pipes should be free from drops

Table 9-6. Size of Piping for Storm Water Only

Diameter of pipe (inches)	Maximum Drained Area in Square Feet		
	A Fall, ⅛ inch per foot	B Fall, ¼ inch per foot	C Fall, ½ inch per foot
2	250	350	500
2½	450	600	900
3	700	1000	1500
4	1500	2100	3000
5	2700	3800	5500
6	4300	6100	9000
8	9600	13,000	19,000
10	16,500	24,000	35,000
12	27,000	40,000	56,000

or sags, or such pipes should be graded and connected as to drip back by gravity to a soil or waste pipe. Where vent pipes connect to a horizontal soil or waste pipe, the vent branch should be taken off above the center line of the pipe, and the vent pipe should rise vertically or at an angle of 45° to the vertical before offsetting horizontally or connecting to the branch, main waste, or soil vent.

What is the required size of the vent?

Answer: The required size of the vent should be determined on the basis of the size of the soil or waste stack, the number of fixture units connected to the vent, and the developed length of the pipe, in accordance with Table 9-7. Vents should be at least 1½ in. in diameter. The diameter of every vent stack should be at least one-half the diameter of the soil or waste stack served. In determining the developed length of vent pipes, the vent stack and branches should be considered continuous.

Where main stacks are grouped together at the top of a structure into one pipe which extends through the roof, such combined vent should be at least equal in area to 75 percent of the sum of the areas of the stacks connecting into such combined vent.

Where should main vents be connected?

Answer: Main vents or vent stacks should connect at their base to the main soil or waste pipe at least 3 ft. below the lowest vent branch. The size of the connection should be as prescribed earlier.

Table 9-7. Vent Stacks and Branches

Diameter of Pipe-inches	Max. number of fixture units	Max. length in feet
1¼	1	45
1½	8	60
2	24	120
2½	48	180
3	84	212
4	256	300
5	600	390
6	1380	510
8	3600	750
10	no limit	no limit
12	no limit	no limit

Stacks should extend undiminished and unincreased in size above the roof, or should be reconnected with the main soil or waste stacks at least 3 ft. above the highest fixture branch. Wherever possible, the base of the vent should receive the wash of the adjoining soil or waste.

What are the rules for offsets in soil, waste, and vent stacks?

Answer: When cast-iron bell-and-spigot pipe is used, offsets in soil and waste stacks above the highest fixture connection and offsets in vent stacks and connections of these stacks to a soil or waste pipe at the bottom, or to the house drain, should be made at an angle of at least 45° to the horizontal. Where it is impractical because of structural conditions to provide a 45° angle, authorities may permit a reduction in the angle under such conditions as they may prescribe, and when it constitutes a vent extension of the vertical waste from the two fixtures. It should be installed with a sanitary cross and not closer than 6 in. to the dip of either trap, each trap to be within 2 ft. from the unit vent. This also applies to a horizontal connection if the common vent is taken off at the point of intersection of the fixture branches.

What are the requirements as to materials in plumbing fixtures?

Answer: Plumbing fixtures should be made of impervious materials with a smooth surface that is easily kept clean. Water closet bowls and traps should be made of glazed vitreous earthenware, in one piece, and should be of such form as to hold a sufficient quantity of water when filled to the trap overflow. To prevent fouling of the surfaces, such bowls and traps should be provided with integral flushing rims constructed to flush the entire interior of the bowl. Urinals should be made of glazed earthenware.

What are the rules as to location of water closets?

Answer: Outside location of water closets is commonly prohibited. Water closet accommodations should be placed inside the structures which they serve, except as provided for temporary privies, or privies to be used where no public sewer is available. Whenever a street sewer connection is available, it is unlawful to replace an inside water closet with an outside water closet.

What types of water closets are prohibited?

Answer: It is unlawful to have pans, plungers, offset washout and washout, or other water closets having unventilated spaces or walls which are not thoroughly washed out at each flushing.

What are the rules on flushing and overflow of water closets?

Answer: Every water closet or urinal should be flushed from a separate flush tank or through an approved flush valve. It is unlawful to connect water closets or urinals directly to a water supply system, except through approved flush valves located to prevent pollution of the water supply. Overflows of flush tanks may discharge into water closets or urinals, but it is unlawful to connect such overflows with any part of the drainage system.

What flush pipe sizes are required for use on water closets?

Answer: Water-closet flush pipes should be at least 1 ¼ in. in diameter, and urinal flush pipes should be at least 1 in. in diameter.

What are the rules with regard to the use of antisiphon devices on fixtures?

Answer: Wherever the supply to a fixture is introduced below the overflow level, the supply should be provided with an approved vacuum breaker that will prevent the siphoning of water from such fixture into the supply piping.

What is the required capacity of water-closet flush tanks?

Answer: Each water closet should be supplied with at least 4 gals. at each flushing, and flush tanks should be of sufficient capacity to supply the required volume. Each urinal should be supplied with at least 2 gals. at each flushing, and flush tanks should be of sufficient capacity to supply the required volume.

What are the rules for determining the number of toilets required in a public building?

Answer: Every office building, school, store, warehouse, manufacturing establishment, or other structure where workmen or workwomen are or will be employed, should be provided with at least one water closet. Water closets should be provided for each sex according to Table 9-8. The number of water closets to be

231

provided for each sex should, in every case, be based upon the maximum number of persons of that sex employed at any one time on the given floor, or in the structure for which such closets are provided.

Table 9-8. Number of Water Closets Required

Number of persons	Number of closets	Ratio
1–15	1	1 for 15
16–35	2	1 for 17½
36–55	3	1 for 18⅓
56–80	4	1 for 20
81–110	5	1 for 22
111–150	6	1 for 25
151–190	7	1 for 27½

What are the requirements as to location of water closets?

Answer: Water closets should be readily accessible to the persons who will use them. It is usually unlawful to locate water closets more than one floor above or below the regular working place of the persons using them, except authorities may determine locations in warehouses, garages, and similar structures of low occupancy. The location requirement is inapplicable when passenger elevators are provided for employees to go to the floors where toilets are located.

What are the rules as to installation of traps in plumbing fixtures?

Answer: Each fixture should be separately trapped as close to the fixture as possible, except that a battery of two or three laundry trays, one sink, and two laundry trays or two compartment sinks may connect with a single trap when the outlets are 2 in. or less. Traps should be as near to the fixture as possible, but at least within 2 ft. developed length from the outlet. It is unlawful to discharge the waste from a bathtub or other fixture into the water-closet trap or bend. It is unlawful to double-trap fixtures.

What is the required design for fixture traps?

Answer: Traps should be self-cleaning and water-sealed, and have a scouring action. Traps for bathtubs, lavatories, sinks, and other similar fixtures should be integral or of lead, brass, plastic, cast iron, or galvanized malleable iron. Traps should have a full-size bore and a smooth interior waterway such that a solid ball, $\frac{1}{4}$-in. smaller in diameter than the specified diameter of the trap, will pass freely from the outlet end entirely through the seal trap. The minimum diameter given is for the soil or waste branch, ·except that in the case of water closets, the required minimum is $2\frac{1}{2}$ in. In cases other than fixtures, the size of the trap should be the same as the size of the discharge pipe connecting thereto. Some codes permit use of plastic traps.

What is the minimum water seal of a fixture trap?
Answer: Fixture traps should have a water seal of at least 2 in.

What are the rules as to setting and protection of fixture traps?
Answer: Traps should be set true with respect to their water seals and protected from frost and evaporation.

What is the required construction for back-water valves?
Answer: Back-water valves should have all bearing parts made of corrosion-resisting metal, and the valves should be constructed to ensure a positive mechanical seal and remain closed, except when discharging wastes. Back-water valves should be the approved type.

What types of traps are prohibited in a plumbing system?
Answer: Full "S" traps and bell traps are prohibited. Traps having covers, hand holes, or clean-outs held in place by lugs or bolts acting as interceptors for grease, or similar substances, may be used if such traps are approved by the board. Allowable fixture traps are shown in Fig. 9-2.

What type of clean-outs is required in fixture traps?
Answer: Easily accessible clean-outs should be provided at the foot of each vertical waste, soil stack, or inside leader, on all hand

233

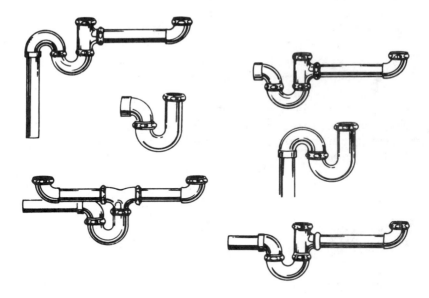

Fig. 9-2. Typical fixture traps.

holes of running traps, on all exposed or accessible fixture traps (except earthenware traps), and at each change of direction of horizontal runs. Clean-outs should be of the same nominal size as the pipes up to 4 in., and such clean-outs shall be at least 4 in. for larger pipes. The maximum distance between the clean-outs in horizontal soil lines should be 100 ft. A typical sewer clean-out is illustrated in Fig. 9-3.

What is considered a clean-out equivalent in a plumbing system?

Answer: If a fixture trap or a fixture with a trap that is integral can be easily removed without damaging or disturbing the roughing-in work, the device can be designated as a clean-out equivalent—but only if there is not more than a single 90° bend in the line that is subject to be rodded. In a single-story building where sink or lavatory traps are easily removed and are accessible, these traps may be considered as clean-out equivalents.

234

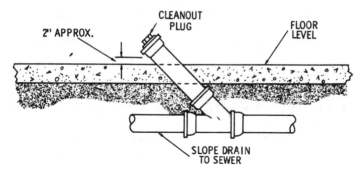

Fig. 9-3. A typical clean-out in a soil-pipe sewer.

How should swimming pools be drained?

Answer: Pools should be provided with a drain outlet located so that the entire pool can be emptied. Pools should also be supplied with an overflow at the high-water line, with the drains at least 3 in. in diameter and trapped before connecting with the drainage system. The trap should be vented. Such overflow should be connected to the inlet side of the trap and on the sewer side of the valve on the emptying drain. Drain and circulating outlets should be fitted with a device to reduce the vortex. The spaces around the pool should be drained to prevent the water from draining into the pool. The drains in the gutter may also serve as overflows. The size of the drain and vent connections should be determined by the capacity of the pool when filled to the overflow level. The diameter of the trap should be at least the diameter of the drain pipe.

What method of water circulation should be provided in swimming pools?

Answer: Pools should be equipped to provide a continuous supply of clear wholesome water at the rate of 20 gals. per hour for each bather using the pool in any one hour. The supply may be either fresh water from an approved water supply system, or such supply may be recirculated if approved means are provided for filtering and sterilizing the water before the water is reintroduced into the pool. The inlets should be located to circulate the water over the entire area of the pool.

The piping of the recirculating system should be kept entirely separate from the city or domestic supply system. Sterilizing and filtration equipment should be adequate to keep the pool in a sanitary condition at all times. Adequate shower-bath and toilet accommodations, conveniently located for the use of the bathers, should be provided for all pools.

Should swimming pools be provided with sterilization and filtration equipment?
Answer: Yes. Sterilizing and filtration equipment should be adequate to keep the pool in a sanitary condition at all times.

What are the rules as to provisions for shower bath and toilet facilities in connection with the operation of swimming pools?
Answer: Adequate shower-bath and toilet accommodations, conveniently located for the use of the bathers, should be provided for all pools.

When does an oil burner pump require a suction line only?
Answer: When the bottom of the oil storage tank is above the burner pump.

When an oil storage tank is installed inside a building, is it necessary to vent it?
Answer: Yes, the vent should be extended above the roof line of the building.

Why should one end of a buried oil tank be slightly lower than the other end?
Answer: To let any moisture accumulate at the low end.

Should the suction line from a pump be installed at the high or the low end of the tank?
Answer: At the high end.

What size pipe is needed to supply a furnace using 185,000 Btu/hr. if the gas heating value is 1,000 and the meter is 40 ft. from the furnace?
Answer: 1-in. pipe.

If a manometer shows a low gas pressure in a building, what is the first item that should be checked?
Answer: The vent from the pressure regulating valve.

At what temperature will propane and butane vaporize?
Answer: Propane vaporizes at − 44° F, butane at 32° F.

Why is LP gas more dangerous to use than natural gas?
Answer: If LP gas, which is heavier than air, should leak from its container or piping, it will collect in a low place in a room or building or in the ground, needing only a spark to cause a fire or an explosion.

Which gas, propane or butane, is more suitable for winter use in the extreme northern United States?
Answer: Propane.

Where should LP gas cylinders be stored?
Answer: Outside, in an open building.

A manometer connected to a gas opening shows a pressure of 2.40 on each side of the tube. What is the actual pressure in the piping?
Answer: 4.80 (water column).

What does a symbol such as mean on a blueprint?
Answer: It means that a detailed drawing of an area will be found on sheet 8, detail 10.

Why should the plumber and pipefitter learn to make good isometric drawings?
Answer: A good isometric drawing will show almost every fitting needed on a job.

What does "invert" mean, applied to soilpipe?
Answer: The inside bottom of the pipe.

237

Checking elevations with an instrument level, with the rod placed on the bench mark, the reading is 6.74. If the bench mark is 820.16, what is the H.I.?
Answer: 826.90

The invert elevation of a pipe is to be at 817.50 and the H.I. of the instrument is 826.90. If the rod is placed on the invert of the pipe, what will be the reading seen through the instrument when the pipe is at the correct elevation?
Answer: 9.40

Why does a plumber need fixture rough-in drawings?
Answer: Rough-in drawings show where the water and waste openings must be "roughed-in," as well as the location of any necessary backing boards or other information in order for the fixtures to be connected properly when the job is finished.

If a job will have approximately thirty 4-in., twelve 3-in. and twelve 2-in. soilpipe joints, how much lead and oakum will be needed?
Answer:

180 lbs. lead	30	12	12	120
	× 4	× 3	× 2	36
18 lbs. oakum	120	36	24	24
				180

REFRIGERATION AND AIR-CONDITIONING SYSTEMS

Name the two basic principles that govern all refrigeration systems.
Answer:
1. A liquid absorbs heat when it boils or evaporates to a gas.
2. As vapor or gas condenses to a liquid form, heat is released.

Why is a sight glass installed in the liquid line?
Answer: To indicate a shortage of refrigerant.

When the unit is in continuous operation, what does low pressure on the evaporator side indicate?
Answer: A leaky or stuck expansion valve needle.

If air flow to and from the condenser is blocked in an air cooled system, what will be the result?
Answer: High head pressure.

Name two causes of a hissing sound at the expansion valve.
Answer: The refrigerant level is too low or the expansion valve needle is stuck open.

Is overcharging a system with refrigerant harmful to the system?
Answer: Yes. Overcharging will cause high head pressure.

What percentage of humidity is generally considered desirable in order to ensure comfort?
Answer: From 30 to 50 percent.

What does a warm or hot liquid line indicate?
Answer: A shortage of refrigerant.

Flow is always from a———to a———pressure area.
Answer: High to low.

What change takes place in the refrigerant when it passes through the evaporator?
Answer: It absorbs heat and is completely vaporized, changing from a liquid to a cold gas.

Why is a compressor necessary in an air-conditioning system?
Answer: The pressure on the refrigerant must be raised so that it can be forced through the condenser and the expansion valve.

What change takes place in the refrigerant as it passes through the expansion valve?
Answer: The refrigerant expands and is partly vaporized; as it

expands, it is changed from a hot liquid to a cold liquid plus vapor mixture.

When the refrigerant enters the air cooled condenser, is the refrigerant hotter or colder than the air entering the condenser?
Answer: Hotter.

Why is a make-up water valve installed in a cooling tower?
Answer: To replace water lost by evaporation.

STEAM HEATING SYSTEMS

Does steam travel faster or slower than other fluid mediums through a heating system?
Answer: Faster.

How can the heat output from steam heating units be raised?
Answer: By raising the steam pressure.

What are the principal advantages of a one-pipe steam system?
Answer: It is dependable and the initial cost is low.

In what type system does the steam and condensate flow in the same direction?
Answer: In a parallel flow system.

An————pattern type radiator valve should always be used on a one pipe steam system. Why?
Answer: Angle, because the steam must enter the radiator, and the condensate must leave through the same valve.

Radiator valves can be used as throttling valves on a one pipe steam system. True or False? Why?
Answer: False, for two reasons: (1) noise would be created; (2) condensate could not return to the boiler.

What is a Hartford loop and why is it used?
Answer: It is a pressure balancing loop which introduces full

boiler pressure on the return side of the boiler to prevent reversed circulation, or water leaving the boiler through the return piping.

In order to be effective, what size should a Hartford loop be? How should it be connected?

Answer:
1. The loop should be the full size of the return main.
2. The horizontal *close* nipple should be installed 2 in. below the boiler water line.

Before steam can enter the piping of a one-pipe system ———— must be eliminated. Why?

Answer:
1. Air.
2. Because air in the radiators or piping will block the flow of steam.

Why should an end-of-main vent be installed on large one-pipe steam systems?
Answer: To assure quick venting of the air in a horizontal main.

What is the basic purpose of an air vent?
Answer: It permits the passage of air while blocking the flow of steam and water.

Why is it incorrect to install an end-of-main vent on the last fitting at the end of the steam main?
Answer: Because the high pressure caused by water surge could damage the float in the vent.

What can be done to ensure that steam will enter all the radiators in a system at the same time?
Answer: Adjustable-port air vents should be installed on each radiator.

What is the function of a vacuum-type air vent?

Answer: It prevents the return of air, through the vent valve, into the system.

The common definition of a small heating system is one in which the total heat loss is not more than————.
Answer: 100,000 Btu/hr.

In common practice, the end of the steam supply main should not be less than————above the boiler water line.
Answer: 18 in.

On larger systems it is common practice to keep the end of the steam supply main————in. above the boiler water line.
Answer: 28.

In a one-pipe steam system to ensure the proper flow of steam, air, and condensate, the steam supply and dry return mains should slope (pitch)——————————in the direction of flow of the condensate.
Answer: One inch in 20 ft.

How much slope does the wet return require?
Answer: None.

In what type system does the steam flow in the opposite direction to the flow of condensate?
Answer: In a counter-flow system.

What is the correct pitch for an upfeed riser that is not dripped into the wet return?
Answer: ½ in. per foot.

A downfeed runout should be taken from the (top) (bottom) of the main?
Answer: Bottom.

A one-pipe system with the distribution main installed above the radiators is called a————system.
Answer: Downfeed.

242

What is the function of a float or thermostatic trap?
Answer: It discharges air and condensate into the return while blocking the flow of steam into the return.

Why is a check valve not a workable alternative to a Hartford loop connection?
Answer: Because a foreign object could become lodged under the check valve, preventing it from seating properly.

What does "flash" mean when applied to hot water?
Answer: Water at high temperature, above 210°, will change into steam when the pressure of the water is reduced.

What type of valve should be used for a radiator supply valve in a two-pipe steam system?
Answer: A globe valve.

Why is a cooling leg sometimes necessary when a thermostatic trap is used?
Answer: To permit the condensate to cool sufficiently to open the trap.

Are cooling legs needed for a float and thermostatic trap?
Answer: No.

STEAM HEATING SYSTEM DESIGN

What is a vapor system?
Answer: A system that operates at pressures ranging from low pressure to vacuum.

What is the pressure range of a low-pressure system?
Answer: 0 to 15 PSIG.

What is the pressure range of a high-pressure system?
Answer: Pressures above 15 PSIG.

A heating system should be designed to operate at approximately————the design load during an average winter.
Answer: One-half.

How should the header on a boiler be sized?
Answer: It should be sized to carry the maximum load that must be carried by any one part of it.

A supply main for a one-pipe system should be at least————in size.
Answer: 2 in.

At the point where a supply main is decreased in size, an————————is the correct fitting to use.
Answer: Eccentric reducer.

What is the advantage in using a two-circuit main with a one-pipe system?
Answer: Quick and uniform delivery of heat.

For a two-pipe system, the minimum pitch or slope for steam and return mains should be not less than——————————.
Answer: ¼ in. per foot.

What is the minimum pitch for horizontal run-outs and risers in a two-pipe system?
Answer: ½ in. per foot.

If the run-out is over 8 ft. in length and the minimum pitch cannot be obtained, what must be done?
Answer: The pipe size must be increased to one pipe size larger than called for in the capacity table.

HOT-WATER HEATING SYSTEMS

Name the three ways in which heat is transmitted.
Answer: Conduction, convection, and radiation.

1. Psi means———?
2. Psig means———?
Answer:
1. pounds per square inch.
2. pounds per square inch gauge.

Why does water circulate in a gravity-type system?

Answer: Because hot water is lighter and less dense than cold water, and rises. Cold water, being denser and heavier than hot water, drops, thus establishing circulation.

Why are balancing cocks used in hot-water heating systems?

Answer: To balance the flow, thus ensuring that hot water will be forced through each unit of radiation in the system.

What is the principal advantage in a reversed-return system?

Answer: The actual developed length of the supply and return piping to each unit of radiation is the same, resulting in a balanced system.

Why is an expansion tank necessary in a closed hot-water heating system?

Answer: To permit the expansion and compression that takes place as water is heated.

What are the principal advantages in the use of special air control fittings?

Answer: Special air control fittings help eliminate the air from piping and radiation and channel the air into the compression (expansion) tank.

What is the normal workable ratio of water-to-air in an expansion tank?

Answer: ⅓ to ½ water; the balance, air.

What is meant by a "waterlogged" expansion tank?

Answer: A tank completely filled with water.

245

Why are air vents installed in high points of a hot-water heating system?

Answer: On initial start-up of a system, or after draining a system down, air tends to collect or be pushed to the high points in a system. This air must be vented to permit the circulation of water.

What happens in a heating system when an expansion tank becomes waterlogged?

Answer: There is no air for the water to expand or compress against, and the pressure buildup as the water is heated will cause the relief valve to open and discharge the excess water.

Water heated from 40° to 200° will expand approximately——%.
Answer: 4%.

A minimum of two aquastats should be installed on a hot-water boiler, one to serve as the————, one to serve as the————control.
Answer: Operating control, high-limit control.

Why should valves be installed on the inlet and discharge sides of circulating pumps?

Answer: To permit removal and replacement or repair of the pump without draining the system.

When radiant heat piping is installed in concrete floors, the maximum water temperature should never exceed ———°.
Answer: 85°.

What is the maximum recommended distance between coils in a radiant heat panel?
Answer: 12 in.

What is the percentage of radiant heat emitted by (a) ceiling panels? (b) floor panels?
Answer: (a) 65%.
(b) 50%.

Which type of coil is best when a constant panel surface temperature is required?
Answer: A grid-type coil.

What is the recommended maximum length of a floor coil using 1/2-in. tubing.?
Answer: 180 ft.

BOILER FITTINGS

What is the function of a safety (relief) valve on a boiler?
Answer: To open and relieve excess pressure in case of a malfunction.

How does a low water cut-off act to provide protection in an emergency?
Answer: A low water cut-off interrupts the firing circuit of a boiler.

What is the purpose of a stop-check valve?
Answer: When two or more boilers are connected to a common header, a stop-check valve in a boiler header prevents the backflow of steam into the boiler in the event of failure of that boiler.

What is the purpose of a blow-off valve?
Answer: It is used to drain off impurities from the lowest point of the boiler.

Why are water gauges installed on steam boilers?
Answer: To give a visual indication of the water level in the boiler.

Why is it desirable to install a "pigtail" between the steam gauge and the boiler?
Answer: To prevent live steam from damaging the gauge.

Why is an injector used on some steam boilers?

247

Answer: An injector uses a steam jet to force water into a steam boiler against the boiler pressure.

Why are fusible plugs used on some boilers?
Answer: To protect the boiler in case of a low water condition.

What is the purpose of a steam loop?
Answer: It is used to return condensate to the boiler.

Name two types of pumps used in steam heating systems.
Answer: Condensate pumps and vacuum pumps.

PLANNING A HEATING SYSTEM

What is the "U" factor?
Answer: A value known as a "coefficient of heat transmission."

What does the U factor represent?
Answer: The time rate of heat flow in Btu/hr. for one square foot of surface with a temperature difference of one degree F between the air on one side and the air on the other.

What is the outside design temperature?
Answer: A temperature that will normally be reached during extreme cold weather.

What is the design temperature difference?
Answer: It is the variation between the outside design temperature and the desired indoor temperature.

How is the heat loss determination made?
Answer: List the design temperature difference on the tabulation sheet and multiply the difference by the U factor to determine the heat loss per square foot.

What does EDR mean?
Answer: Equivalent direct radiation.

One sq. ft. of EDR = —————?
Answer: 240 Btu/hr.

If 20,400 Btu/hr. are required to heat a room, how many sq. ft. of radiation are required?
Answer: 85 sq. ft. of EDR capacity.

Where is baseboard radiation normally installed?
Answer: Along an outside wall.

WELDING AND BRAZING

How are brazing temperatures different from welding temperatures?
Answer: Brazing alloy is applied at a temperature below the melting temperature of the metal being brazed. Welding is done at a temperature at or above the melting point of the metal being welded.

What change takes place when malleable iron is heated above 1575° F?
Answer: It reverts to cast iron and is no longer ductile.

Is brazing of stainless steel recommended?
Answer: It is difficult to braze stainless steel with copper-zinc (brass) alloys. Stainless steel can be readily brazed with silver alloys.

Does silver alloy brazing (silver soldering) require the use of flux?
Answer: Yes, in most instances. Copper to copper joints do not require flux if the metals are clean and bright.

The end of a pipe should be cut and beveled to an angle of approximately ————° for a welded joint.
Answer: 35°.

How many tackwelds should be made when welding a 4-in. joint?

Answer: Four.

In what order should these tackwelds be made?
Answer: 1-3; 2-4.

Why should an oxygen cylinder valve be opened fully?
Answer: Because it is a double-seated valve and may leak unless fully opened or fully closed.

Why should an acetylene cylinder valve never be opened more than 11/2 turns?
Answer: In order that it may be shut off quickly in an emergency.

Why must oxygen never be brought into contact with grease or oil?
Answer: Because oil or grease may ignite violently if brought into contact with oxygen.

Why is a two-stage regulator the best type to use?
Answer: Because it will deliver constant pressure and require less maintenance.

Index

251

The Audel®
Mail Order
Bookstore

Here's an opportunity to order the valuable books you may have missed
before and to build your own personal, comprehensive library of Audel books.
You can choose from an extensive selection of technical guides and reference
books. They will provide access to the same sources the experts use, put all
the answers at your fingertips, and give you the know-how to complete even
the most complicated building or repairing job, in the same professional way.

Each volume:

- **Fully illustrated**
- **Packed with up-to-date facts and figures**
- **Completely indexed for easy reference**

APPLIANCES
HOME APPLIANCE SERVICING, 4th Edition
A practical book for electric & gas servicemen, mechanics & dealers. Covers the principles, servicing, and repairing of home appliances. 592 pages $5\frac{1}{2} \times 8\frac{1}{4}$; hardbound. **Price: $15.95**

REFRIGERATION: HOME AND COMMERCIAL
Covers the whole realm of refrigeration equipment from fractional-horsepower water coolers
through domestic refrigerators to multiton commercial installations. 656 pages; $5\frac{1}{2} \times 8\frac{1}{4}$;
hardbound. **Price: $16.95**

AIR CONDITIONING: HOME AND COMMERCIAL
A concise collection of basic information, tables, and charts for those interested in understanding
troubleshooting, and repairing home air-conditioners and commercial installations. 464 pages;
$5\frac{1}{2} \times 8\frac{1}{4}$; hardbound. **Price: $14.95**

OIL BURNERS, 4th Edition
Provides complete information on all types of oil burners and associated equipment. Discusses
burners—blowers—ignition transformers—electrodes—nozzles—fuel pumps—filters—controls.
Installation and maintenance are stressed. 320 pages; $5\frac{1}{2} \times 8\frac{1}{4}$; hardbound. **Price: $12.95**

AUTOMOTIVE
AUTOMOBILE REPAIR GUIDE, 4th Edition
A practical reference for auto mechanics, servicemen, trainees, and owners. Explains theory, con-
struction, and servicing of modern domestic motorcars. 800 pages; $5\frac{1}{2} \times 8\frac{1}{4}$; hardbound.
Price: $14.95

Use the order coupon on the back of this book.
All prices are subject to change without notice.

AUTOMOTIVE AIR CONDITIONING

You can easily perform most all service procedures you've been paying for in the past. This book covers the systems built by the major manufacturers, even after-market installations. Contents: introduction—refrigerant—tools—air conditioning circuit—general service procedures—electrical systems—the cooling systems—system diagnosis—electrical diagnosis—troubleshooting. 232 pages; 5½ × 8¼; softcover. **Price: $7.95**

DIESEL ENGINE MANUAL, 4th Edition

A practical guide covering the theory, operation and maintenance of modern diesel engines. Explains diesel principles—valves—timing—fuel pumps—pistons and rings—cylinders—lubrication—cooling system—fuel oil and more. 480 pages; 5½ × 8¼; hardbound. **Price: $12.95**

GAS ENGINE MANUAL, 2nd Edition

A completely practical book covering the construction, operation, and repair of all types of modern gas engines. 400 pages; 5½ × 8¼; hardbound. **Price: $9.95**

SMALL GASOLINE ENGINES

A new manual providing practical and theoretical information for those who want to maintain and overhaul two- and four-cycle engines such as lawn mowers, edgers, snowblowers, outboard motors, electrical generators, and other equipment using engines up to 10 horsepower. 624 pp; 5½ × 8¼; hardbound. **Price: $15.95**

TRUCK GUIDE—3 Vols.

Three all-new volumes provide a primary source of practical information on truck operation and maintenance. Covers everything from basic principles (truck classification, construction components, and capabilities) to troubleshooting and repair. 1584 pages; 5½ × 8¼; hardbound. **Price: $41.85**
   Volume 1
   ENGINES: **$14.95**
   Volume 2
   ENGINE AUXILIARY SYSTEMS: **$14.95**
   Volume 3
   TRANSMISSIONS, STEERING AND BRAKES: **$14.95**

BUILDING AND MAINTENANCE
ANSWERS ON BLUEPRINT READING, 3rd Edition

Covers all types of blueprint reading for mechanics and builders. This book reveals the secret language of blueprints, step by step in easy stages. 312 pages; 5½ × 8¼; hardbound. **Price: $9.95**

BUILDING MAINTENANCE, 2nd Edition

Covers all the practical aspects of building maintenance. Painting and decorating; plumbing and pipe fitting; carpentry; heating maintenance; custodial practices and more. (A book for building owners, managers, and maintenance personnel.) 384 pages; 5½ × 8¼; hardbound. **Price: $9.95**

COMPLETE BUILDING CONSTRUCTION

At last—a one volume instruction manual to show you how to construct a frame or brick building from the footings to the ridge. Build your own garage, tool shed, other outbuildings—even your own house or place of business. Building construction tells you how to lay out the building and excavation lines on the lot; how to make concrete forms and pour the footings and foundation; how to make concrete slabs, walks, and driveways; how to lay concrete block, brick and tile; how to build your own fireplace and chimney. It's one of the newest Audel books, clearly written by experts in each field and ready to help you every step of the way. 800 pages; 5½ × 8¼; hardbound. **Price: $19.95**

Use the order coupon on the back of this book.
All prices are subject to change without notice.

GARDENING, LANDSCAPING, & GROUNDS MAINTENANCE, 3rd Edition

A comprehensive guide for homeowners and for industrial, municipal, and estate grounds-keepers. Gives information on proper care of annual and perennial flowers, various house plants; greenhouse design and construction; insect and rodent controls; and more. 416 pages; 5½ × 8¼; hardbound. **Price: $15.95**

CARPENTERS & BUILDERS LIBRARY, 5th Edition (4 Vols.)

A practical, illustrated trade assistant on modern construction for carpenters, builders, and all woodworkers. Explains in practical, concise language and Ilustrations all the principles, advances, and shortcuts based on modern practice. How to calculate various jobs. **Price: $39.95**
Volume 1
Tools, steel square, saw filing, joinery cabinets. 384 pages; 5½ × 8¼; hardbound.
Price: $10.95
Volume 2
Mathematics, plans, specifications, estimates. 304 pages. 5½ × 8¼; hardbound.
Price: $10.95
Volume 3
House and roof framing, layout foundations. 304 pages; 5½ × 8¼; hardbound.
Price: $10.95
Volume 4
Doors, windows, stairs, millwork, painting. 368 pages; 5½ × 8¼; hardbound.
Price: $10.95

HEATING, VENTILATING, AND AIR CONDITIONING LIBRARY (3 Vols.)

This three-volume set covers all types of furnaces, ductwork, air conditioners, heat pumps, radiant heaters, and water heaters, including swimming-pool heating systems. **Price: $41.95**
Volume 1
Partial Contents: Heating Fundamentals—Insulation Principles—Heating Fuels—Electric Heating System—Furnace Fundamentals—Gas-Fired Furnaces—Oil-Fired Furnaces—Coal-Fired Furnaces—Electric Furnaces. 614 pages; 5½ × 8¼; hardbound. **Price: $14.95**
Volume 2
Partial Contents: Oil Eurners—Gas Burners—Thermostats and Humidistats—Gas and Oil Controls—Pipes, Pipe Fitting, and Piping Details—Valves and Valve Installations. 560 pages; 5½ × 8¼; hardbound. **Price: $14.95**
Volume 3
Partial Contents: Radiant Heating—Radiators, Convectors, and Unit Heaters—Stoves, Fireplaces, and Chimneys—Water Heaters and Other Appliances—Central Air Conditioning Systems—Humidifiers and Dehumidifiers. 544 pages; 5½ × 8¼; hardbound. **Price: $14.95**

HOME-MAINTENANCE AND REPAIR: Walls, Ceilings, and Floors

Easy-to-follow instructions for sprucing up and repairing the walls, ceiling, and floors of your home. Covers nail pops, plaster repair, painting, paneling, ceiling and bathroom tile, and sound control. 80 pages; 8½ × 11; softcover. **Price: $6.95**

HOME PLUMBING HANDBOOK, 3rd Edition

A complete guide to home plumbing repair and installation, 200 pages; 8½ × 11; softcover.
Price: $8.95

MASONS AND BUILDERS LIBRARY, 2nd Edition—2 Vols.

A practical, illustrated trade assistant on modern construction for bricklayers, stonemasons, cement workers, plasterers, and tile setters. Explains all the principles, advances, and shortcuts based on modern practice—including how to figure and calculate various jobs. **Price: $24.90**
Volume 1
Concrete Block, Tile, Terrazzo. 368 pages; 5½ × 8¼; hardbound. **Price: $12.95**

Use the order coupon on the back of this book.
All prices are subject to change without notice.

Volume 2
Bricklaying, Plastering Rock Masonry, Clay Tile. 384 pages; 5½ × 8¼; hardbound.
Price: $12.95

PAINTING AND DECORATING
This all-inclusive guide to the principles and practice of coating and finishing interior and exterior surfaces is a fundamental sourcebook for the working painter and decorator and an invaluable guide for the serious amateur or building owner. Provides detailed descriptions of materials, pigmenting and mixing procedures, equipment, surface preparation, restoration, repair, and antiquing of all kinds of surfaces. 608 pages; 5½ × 8¼; hardbound. **Price: $18.95**

PLUMBERS AND PIPE FITTERS LIBRARY, 3rd Edition—3 Vols.
A practical, illustrated trade assistant and reference for master plumbers, journeymen and apprentice pipe fitters, gas fitters and helpers, builders, contractors, and engineers. Explains in simple language, illustrations, diagrams, charts, graphs, and pictures the principles of modern plumbing and pipe-fitting practices. **Price: $32.85**

Volume 1
Materials, tools, roughing-in. 320 pages; 5½ × 8¼; hardbound. **Price: $11.95**

Volume 2
Welding, heating, air-conditioning. 384 pages; 5½ × 8¼; hardbound. **Price: $11.95**

Volume 3
Water supply, drainage, calculations. 272 pages; 5½ × 8¼; hardbound. **Price: $11.95**

THE PLUMBERS HANDBOOK, 7th Edition
A pocket manual providing reference material for plumbers and/or pipe fitters. General information sections contain data on cast-iron fittings, copper drainage fittings, plastic pipe, and repair of fixtures. 330 pages; 4 × 6 softcover. **Price: $9.95**

QUESTIONS AND ANSWERS FOR PLUMBERS EXAMINATIONS, 2nd Edition
Answers plumbers' questions about types of fixtures to use, size of pipe to install, design of systems, size and location of septic tank systems, and procedures used in installing material. 256 pages; 5½ × 8¼; softcover. **Price: $8.95**

TREE CARE MANUAL
The conscientious gardener's guide to healthy, beautiful trees. Covers planting, grafting, fertilizing, pruning, and spraying. Tells how to cope with insects, plant diseases, and environmental damage. 224 pages; 8½ × 11; softcover. **Price: $8.95**

UPHOLSTERING
Upholstering is explained for the average householder and apprentice upholsterer. From repairing and regluing of the bare frame, to the final sewing or tacking, for antiques and most modern pieces, this book covers it all. 400 pages; 5½ × 8¼; hardbound. **Price: $12.95**

WOOD FURNITURE: Finishing, Refinishing, Repair
Presents the fundamentals of furniture repair for both veneer and solid wood. Gives complete instructions on refinishing procedures, which includes stripping the old finish, sanding, selecting the finish and using wood fillers. 352 pages; 5½ × 8¼; hardbound. **Price: $9.95**

ELECTRICITY/ELECTRONICS
ELECTRICAL LIBRARY
If you are a student of electricity or a practicing electrician, here is a very important and helpful library you should consider owning. You can learn the basics of electricity, study electric motors and wiring diagrams, learn how to interpret the NEC, and prepare for the electrician's examination by using these books.

Use the order coupon on the back of this book.
All prices are subject to change without notice.

Electric Motors, 4th Edition. 528 pages; 5½ × 8¼; hardbound. **Price: $12.95**

Guide to the 1984 National Electrical Code. 672 pages; 5½ × 8¼; hardbound. **Price: $18.95**

House Wiring, 6th Edition. 256 pages; 5½ × 8¼; hardbound. **Price: $12.95**

Practical Electricity, 4th Edition. 496 pages; 5½ × 8¼; hardbound. **Price: $13.95**

Questions and Answers for Electricians Examinations, 8th Edition. 288 pages; 5½ × 8¼; hardbound. **Price: $12.95**

ELECTRICAL COURSE FOR APPRENTICES AND JOURNEYMEN, 2nd Edition
A study course for apprentice or journeymen electricians. Covers electrical theory and its applications. 448 pages; 5½ × 8¼; hardbound. **Price: $13.95**

FRACTIONAL HORSEPOWER ELECTRIC MOTORS
This new book provides guidance in the selection, installation, operation, maintenance, repair, and replacement of the small-to-moderate size electric motors that power home appliances and over 90 percent of industrial equipment. Provides clear explanations and illustrations of both theory and practice. 352 pages; 5½ × 8¼; hardbound. **Price: $15.95**

TELEVISION SERVICE MANUAL, 5th Edition
Provides the practical information necessary for accurate diagnosis and repair of both black-and-white and color television receivers. 512 pages; 5½ × 8¼; hardbound. **Price: $15.95**

ENGINEERS/MECHANICS/MACHINISTS
MACHINISTS LIBRARY, 4th Edition
Covers the modern machine-shop practice. Tells how to set up and operate lathes, screw and milling machines, shapers, drill presses and all other machine tools. A complete reference library. **Price: $35.85**
Volume 1
Basic Machine Shop. 352 pages; 5½ × 8¼; hardbound. **Price: $12.95**
Volume 2
Machine Shop. 480 pages; 5½ × 8¼; hardbound. **Price: $12.95**
Volume 3
Toolmakers Handy Book. 400 pages; 5½ × 8¼; hardbound. **Price: $12.95**

MECHANICAL TRADES POCKET MANUAL, 2nd Edition
Provides practical reference material for mechanical tradesmen. This handbook covers methods, tools equipment, procedures, and much more. 256 pages; 4 × 6; softcover. **Price: $10.95**

MILLWRIGHTS AND MECHANICS GUIDE, 3rd Edition
Practical information on plant installation, operation, and maintenance for millwrights, mechanics, maintenance men, erectors, riggers, foremen, inspectors, and superintendents. 960 pages; 5½ × 8¼; hardbound. **Price: $19.95**

POWER PLANT ENGINEERS GUIDE, 3rd Edition
The complete steam or diesel power-plant engineer's library. 816 pages; 5½ × 8¼ hardbound. **Price: $16.95**

WELDERS GUIDE, 3rd Edition
This new edition is a practical and concise manual on the theory, practical operation and maintenance of all welding machines. Fully covers both electric and oxy-gas welding. 928 pages; 5½ × 8¼; hardbound. **Price: $19.95**

Use the order coupon on the back of this book.
All prices are subject to change without notice.

WELDER/FITTERS GUIDE
Provides basic training and instruction for those wishing to become welder/fitters. Step-by-step learning sequences are presented from learning about basic tools and aids used in weldment assembly, through simple work practices, to actual fabrication of weldments. 160 pages; $8^{1}/_{2} \times 11$; softcover. **Price: $7.95**

FLUID POWER
PNEUMATICS AND HYDRAULICS, 4th Edition
Fully discusses installation, operation and maintenance of both HYDRAULIC AND PNEUMATIC (air) devices. 496 pages; $5^{1}/_{2} \times 8^{1}/_{4}$; hardbound. **Price: $15.95**

PUMPS, 4th Edition
A detailed book on all types of pumps from the old-fashioned kitchen variety to the most modern types. Covers construction, application, installation, and troubleshooting. 480 pages; $5^{1}/_{2} \times 8^{1}/_{4}$; hardbound. **Price: $14.95**

HYDRAULICS FOR OFF-THE-ROAD EQUIPMENT
Everything you need to know from basic hydraulics to troubleshooting hydraulic systems on off-the-road equipment. Heavy-equipment operators, farmers, fork-lift owners and operators, mechanics—all need this practical, fully illustrated manual. 272 pages; $5^{1}/_{2} \times 8^{1}/_{4}$; hardbound.
Price: $8.95

HOBBY
COMPLETE COURSE IN STAINED GLASS
Written by an outstanding artist in the field of stained glass, this book is dedicated to all who love the beauty of the art. Ten complete lessons describe the required materials, how to obtain them, and explicit directions for making several stained glass projects. 80 pages; $8^{1}/_{2} \times 11$; softbound.
Price: $6.95

Use the order coupon on the back of this book.
All prices are subject to change without notice.

BUILD YOUR OWN AUDEL DO-IT-YOURSELF LIBRARY AT HOME!

Use the handy order coupon today to gain the valuable information you need in all the areas that once required a repairman. Save money and have fun while you learn to service your own air conditioner, automobile, and plumbing. Do your own professional carpentry, masonry, and wood furniture refinishing and repair. Build your own security systems. Find out how to repair your TV or Hi-Fi. Learn landscaping, upholstery, electronics and much, much more.